RUTH WILLIAM

EVOLUTION IN ACTION

EVOLUTION
IN ACTION

BASED ON THE
PATTEN FOUNDATION LECTURES
DELIVERED AT INDIANA UNIVERSITY
IN 1951

Julian Huxley

M.A., D.Sc., F.R.S.

1953
CHATTO & WINDUS
LONDON

Published by
CHATTO AND WINDUS
LONDON

*

CLARKE, IRWIN AND CO. LTD
TORONTO

CONTENTS

Preface   vii

Chapter   *Page*
1 The Process of Evolution   11

2 How Natural Selection Works   38

3 Biological Improvement   62

4 The Development of Mental Activity   85

5 The Path of Biological Progress   112

6 The Human Phase   134

Index   155

ILLUSTRATIONS

For full descriptive captions see plates and text

FIG.   FACING PAGE

1 (A) Recapitulation in man

   (B) The genetic outfit of chromosomes   16
        in a plant

2   The display of the Argus pheasant

                                                  between p. 32
3   Details of the display characters of   *and*   *p.* 33
       the male Argus pheasant

                                                  FACING PAGE

4   Eohippus, the earliest known horse   49

5   Diagram of trends in horse evolution   57

6   Cells from the cerebral cortex of a   80
       mammal

7   Professor Cantril's distorted room.   97
       An illusion showing how we con-
       struct our perceptions on the
       basis of experience

8   A living fossil. The Australian   112
       lung-fish *Neoceratodus*

9   Persistence of type: a fossil ant pre-   129
       served in Baltic amber

PREFACE

In all fields of enquiry, there is the danger of not seeing the wood for the trees. Nowhere is the danger greater than in the field of evolution. My underlying thesis has been that there is a single evolutionary process to be studied, and that the separate aspects of the problem only acquire full significance when considered in relation to the whole. This is particularly true of man and his history. It makes a great difference whether we think of the history of mankind as something wholly apart from the history of the rest of life, or as a continuation of the general evolutionary process, though with special characteristics of its own.

In this little book, I have accordingly attempted to give a rapid survey of the evolutionary process as it looks today to a general biologist. In it, I have tried to stress on the one hand the unity of the process, and on the other its special or unique features. There are mechanisms common to all life, such as the apparatus of heredity—the genetic outfit with its hundreds of genes, the occasional variations in the nature of genes due to mutation, the arrangements for distributing and combining gene-variations provided by sexual recombination. There are common principles, such as the universal principle of natural selection, whereby favourable mutations gradually become incorporated as normal elements in the gene-complex, and the organism is adjusted to its environment. There are common trends, such as adaptation, species-formation, specialization of type over long periods of geological time, and deployment of groups to fill a greater range of places in the economy of nature.

Superimposed on these, there is also the broad tendency towards advance in general efficiency of construction and working. And this involves the appearance of new capacities during the process. Striking examples of these are new ways of life such as flying, and new sensory and mental or cerebral possibilities such as pattern-vision and learning by experience.

Here we pass from the general to the special. Among the special characteristics of the process, we have the emergence of mental capacities to the level where they may begin to affect the future course of events. Then there is the capacity for progress, in the sense of advance which permits further advance instead of leading eventually into blind alleys of specialization. Progress in this sense is unique, since only one progressive line has continued into the present epoch: the line leading to man.

This line is also unique in that it has enabled life to transcend itself, by making possible a second mechanism for continuity and change, in addition to the genetic outfit in the chromosomes. This is man's method of utilizing cumulative experience, which gives him new powers of control over nature and new and more rapid methods of adjustment to changing circumstances.

To attempt this broad survey means drawing on very different branches of knowledge, from genetics and paleontology to animal behaviour and human psychology, with excursions into other subjects such as physiology and even history. It is obvious that no one man can hope to cover all these subjects adequately, and I am sure that many of my statements will be necessarily imperfect expressions of current knowledge. I am also sure that many of them will turn out to be over-simplified. Nevertheless, simplification is sometimes desirable, in order to draw attention to general tendencies. Otherwise, the subject may become obscured in a mass of detail while unifying principles are lost to sight among apparently contradictory particulars.

Furthermore, I have attempted to present a point of view: it is always based on facts, but is in many respects a particular and personal one. I hold strongly that without some knowledge of evolution one cannot hope to arrive at a true picture of human destiny, or even to approach the problem correctly. It is possible that I may have been over-sweeping in some of my conclusions; and I shall probably be attacked for going beyond the boundaries of science. But I am sure that I have been right in formulating general conclusions of this sort. Only so can one hope to have them investigated; and general conclusions about man's origin and destiny are of importance, especially in an age of doubt and transition like the present.

I owe a great deal to discussion with various biological colleagues. Among these, I would specially mention Professor H. J. Muller, Dr. E. B. Ford, F.R.S., Professor Stanley Westoll, F.R.S., and Dr. G. G. Simpson. But they are in no way committed to my particular views, for which I alone am responsible.

The substance of this book was originally delivered as a series of public lectures under the Patten Foundation at Indiana University. I wish to take the opportunity of thanking the authorities there for all the help and encouragement they gave me.

I later adapted my notes to serve as a basis for a series of special talks for the B.B.C. on the same subject.

When I came to prepare the material for publication, various friends urged me to retain this general presentation. I have accordingly utilized the text of the wireless lecture-talks as the primary basis for this book, merely adjusting the spoken to the printed word, and adding a certain number of emendations and amplifications.

London, *May* 1952

CHAPTER I

The Process of Evolution

SCIENCE has two functions: control and comprehension. The comprehension may be of the universe in which we live; or of ourselves; or of the relations between ourselves and our world. Evolutionary science has only been in existence, as a special branch of scientific knowledge, for less than a century. During that time its primary contribution has been to comprehension—first to that of the world around us, and then to that of our own nature. The last few decades have added an increasing comprehension of our position in the universe and our relations with it; and with this, evolutionary science is certainly destined to make an important and increasing contribution to control; its practical application in the affairs of human life is about to begin.

Evolutionary science is a discipline or subject in its own right. But it is the joint product of a number of separate branches of study and learning. Biology provides its central and largest component, but it has also received indispensable contributions from pure physics and chemistry, cosmogony and geology among the natural sciences, and among human studies from history and social science, archeology and prehistory, psychology and anthropology. As a result, the present is the first period in which we have been able to grasp that the universe is a process in time and to get a first glimpse of our true relation with it. We can see ourselves as history, and can see that history in its proper relation with the history of the universe as a whole.

All phenomena have a historical aspect. From the condensation of nebulae to the development of the infant in the womb, from the formation of the earth as a planet to the making of a political decision, they are all processes in time; and they are all interrelated as partial processes within the single universal process of reality. All reality, in fact, *is* evolution, in the perfectly proper sense that it is a one-way process in time; unitary; continuous; irreversible; self-transforming; and generating variety and novelty during its transformations. I am quite aware that many people object to the use of the term evolution for anything but the transformations of living substance. But I think this is undesirably narrow. Some term is undoubtedly needed for the comprehensive process in all its aspects, and no other convenient designation exists at present save that of evolution.[1]

The overall process of evolution in this comprehensive sense comprises three main phases. Although there is continuity between them, they are very distinct in their main features, and represent three sectors of reality, in which the general process of evolution operates in three quite different ways. We may call these three phases the inorganic or, if you like, cosmological; the organic or biological; and the human or psycho-social. The three sectors of the universal process differ radically in their extent, both in space and time, in the methods and mechanisms by which their self-transformations operate, in their rates of change, in the results which they produce, and in the levels of organization which they attain. They also differ in their time-relations. The second phase is only possible on the basis of the first, the third on the basis of the second; so that, although all three are in operation today, their origins succeeded each other in time.

[1] It may be desirable to coin a new term: this I must leave to the philosophers of science. Meanwhile in later chapters I shall, perhaps illogically, use evolution in the restricted sense of biological evolution whenever there is no danger of confusion.

There was a critical point to be surmounted before the second could arise out of the first, or the third out of the second.

The inorganic sector I must deal with extremely briefly. For further details I must refer my readers to standard works like those of Sir James Jeans or Sir Arthur Eddington, or the more recent picture so vividly sketched by Fred Hoyle in his little book *The Nature of the Universe*. The chief points which have a bearing on my theme of evolution seem to me to be these. This sector of reality comprises all the purely physico-chemical aspects of the universe throughout the whole of space, intergalactic as well as interstellar, all the galaxies, all the stars and stellar nebulae. The diameter of that part of it visible with the new 200-inch telescope is nearly a thousand million light-years; and there is a celestial region of unknown size beyond the range of any telescope that we may ever be able to construct. There are over a hundred million visible galaxies; and each of these contains anything from a hundred to ten thousand million stars. Obviously, then, the inorganic sector is by far the largest in spatial extent. It is also the largest in temporal extent: astronomers put the age of our own galaxy at up to five thousand million years—probably rather less—and most of them think the universe as a whole is of about the same age, though some believe it is considerably older.

But the mechanism of its transformation is of the simplest kind—physical, and very occasionally chemical, interaction. The degree of organization to be found in it is correspondingly simple: most of this vast sector consists of nothing but radiations, subatomic particles, and atoms; only here and there in it is matter able to attain the molecular level, and nowhere are its molecules at all large or complicated. Very few of them contain more than half a dozen atoms, as opposed to the many thousands of atoms in the more complex organic molecules found in living substance. Many of the results are extremely large—stars and galaxies; but their organization is of a very low order: the simple spirals of the galaxies, the concentric arrangement of layers in the stars. In the tiny fraction that has turned into planetary systems, the level of organization is higher, but only a little higher. Nowhere in all its vast extent is there any trace of purpose, or even of prospective significance. It is impelled from behind by blind physical forces, a gigantic and chaotic jazz dance of particles and radiations, in which the only overall tendency we have so far been able to detect is that summarized in the Second Law of Thermodynamics—the tendency to run down.

By contrast, the spatial extension of the biological sector is very much restricted. Living substance could not come into being except in that small minority of stars which have produced planetary systems. Within them, it is restricted to that small minority of their planets which are of the right size and in the right stage of their history for complicated self-copying organic molecules to be produced; and in them again to an infinitesimal surface shell. The number of such potential homes of life in our own galaxy is put by a few astronomers as high as a hundred thousand, but by most at only a few thousand or even a few hundreds. Whatever the truth turns out to be, the biological sector, considered spatially as the area occupied by life, cannot at the very outside constitute more than a million-million-millionth part of the extent of the visible universe, and probably much less. And of course the only spot of which we have actual knowledge is our own planet, with the possibility of Mars in addition. On the earth the extension of the biological sector in time appears to be about two thousand million years.

On the other hand, the level of organization reached

is almost infinitely greater than in the preceding sector. The proteins, the most essential chemical constituents of living substance, have molecules with tens or even hundreds of thousands of atoms, all arranged in patterns characteristic for each kind of protein. Each single tiny cell has a highly complex organization of its own, with a nucleus, chromosomes and genes (Fig. 1 (B), p. 16), and other cell-organs, and is built out of a number of different kinds of proteins and other types of chemical units, mostly large and complex. But that is only the beginning, for large higher mammals such as men and whales may have in their bodies over a hundred million million or even over a thousand million million cells of many different types, and organized in the most elaborate patterns. As Professor J. Z. Young has set forth in his recent book, *Doubt and Certainty in Science*, the number of cells in our "thinking parts" alone—the cerebral cortex of our brain—is about seven times the total human population of the world, and their organization is of a scarcely conceivable complexity (Fig. 6, p. 80).

Evolutionary transformation in this sector is brought about by the wholly new method of natural selection, which was not available during the thousands of millions of years before the emergence of living substance. This new method is responsible for the much higher level of organization which evolution here produces, as well as the greater variety of organization. It is also responsible for the much faster tempo of change: quite large changes in biological organization take only a few tens of millions of years; and really major ones, much more radical than any which can have occurred during the entire inorganic phase, only a hundred million or so.

At first sight the biological sector seems full of purpose. Organisms are built as if purposefully designed, and work as if in purposeful pursuit of a conscious aim.

But the truth lies in those two words "as if." As the genius of Darwin showed, the purpose is only an apparent one. However, this at least implies prospective significance. Natural selection operates in relation to the future—the future survival of the individual and the species. And its products, in the shape of actual animals and plants, are correspondingly oriented towards the future, in their structure, their mode of working, and their behaviour. A few of the later products of evolution, notably the higher mammals, do show true purpose, in the sense of the awareness of a goal. But the purpose is confined to individuals and their actions. It does not enter into the basic machinery of the evolutionary process, although it helps the realization of its results. Evolution in the biological phase is still impelled from behind; but the process is now structured so as to be directed forwards.

The human phase of evolution, what I have called the psycho-social sector, is again enormously more limited in spatial extent. On this earth it is restricted to one among over a million species of organisms; elsewhere anything that could be called a psycho-social sector assuredly cannot have been attained in more than a very small fraction—perhaps a hundredth, perhaps only a ten-thousandth—of the planets habitable by some kind of life. It is still more limited in its temporal

FIG. 1 (A).—*Recapitulation* (p. 21). Model of human embryo (6 weeks old). This human being, 0.4 inch long, has a short tail; the slit on the neck is the last remainder of the gill-clefts which were prominent in the three-weeks embryo.

FIG. 1 (B).—*The genetic outfit* (p. 26). The chromosomes of a dividing cell of the plant *Fritillaria*. They have divided longitudinally after self-duplication and the daughter-chromosomes are now moving apart, so that each cell will receive an identical set of genes.

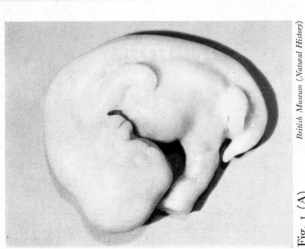

Fig. 1 (A)

British Museum (Natural History)

Fig. 1 (B)

Darlington and La Cour

extent: its existence on this earth, from its first dim dawn to the present, occupies only one-half of one-tenth per cent. of the history of life as a whole; and it has only operated at anything like full swing for perhaps a tenth of that tiny fraction of time.

Once again, a new main method of transformation has become available in this sector—the method of cumulative experience combined with conscious purpose. This has produced a new kind of result, in the shape of transmissible cultures; the main unit of evolution in the human phase is not the biological species, but the stream of culture, and genetic advance has taken a back seat as compared with changes in the transmissible techniques of cultural advance—arts and skills, moral codes and religious beliefs, and above all knowledge and ideas. It has also meant not only a more rapid tempo, but a new kind of tempo—an acceleration instead of a more or less steady average rate over long periods. In the long prologue of human evolution, each major change demanded something of the order of a hundred thousand years; immediately after the end of the Ice Age, something like a thousand years; during much of recorded history, the time-unit of major change was around a century; while recently it has been reduced to a decade or so. And again correlated with this increased tempo of change, we find an enormous increase in the variety of the results produced and in the levels of organization attained. In a way most important, purpose has now entered the process of transformation itself; both the mechanisms of psycho-social evolution and its products have a truly purposeful component, and evolution in this sector is pulled on consciously from in front as well as being impelled blindly from behind.

This, however, I shall be dealing with in my final chapter. Here I want to give a preliminary statement of the purely biological problem. Description and definition are the first steps in science, so I shall try to describe as concisely as possible the overall picture, or at least the relevant features, of the biological phase of reality that we have reached today. At the present time, over a million species of animals have been described, and well over a third of that number of plants, all different and distinct, while every year several thousand new species are being discovered and given names. They extend into every nook and cranny of the environment possible to life, from the polar regions to the equator, from the high mountains to the black marine abyss, from hot springs not much below boiling point to the oxygenless interiors of other animals. They exploit their environment in every possible way. To take only animals, there are species which feed entirely on flesh, on wood, on excrement, on nectar, on feathers, on the contents of others' intestines, on one particular kind of fruit or leaf. And each and every species is adapted, often in the most astonishing fashion, to its environment and its way of life. Think of the duck's webbed feet, the camel's stomach, or the luminous organs of deep-sea fish. There is no need to multiply examples: every animal and plant is from one aspect an organized bundle of adaptations—of structure, physiology and behaviour; and the organization of the whole bundle is itself an adaptation.

Living things fall naturally into a number of groups, each with its own plan of structure and working. Here I can only mention some of the more striking variations. The first grouping is into animals, plants and viruses, each characterized by a radically different chemical way of life. The first thing that strikes one about the animal group is the great variety of plans of construction and operation within it. Thus, the protozoa are all single-celled, or, more accurately, are all based on the single cell as unit: the sponges are all mouthless filter-feeders: the sea-anemones and jellyfish and their relatives do possess a mouth, but have no head, and are built on a radial plan without distinction of ventral or dorsal. There are the echinoderms, like starfish and sea-urchins, which have secondarily lost their bilateral symmetry for a radial construction. There are various types of worms; and the great group of molluscs, with clams, snails and cuttlefish. The two highest groups are the arthropods—insects, crustaceans and spiders—and the vertebrates, from fish to men. They both have an elaborate organization, with head, limbs, eyes, heart and brain. But while the arthropods have many limbs and have a dead horny external skeleton for their mechanical framework, the vertebrates, when they once develop limbs, have two pairs only, and their skeleton is a living tissue, of cartilage or bone, and in higher forms is entirely internal, leaving the surface of the body sensitive and free.

The plants are perhaps less varied. Certainly they never reach the complexity of some animals. They divide first into the minute bacteria: the true fungi— moulds and toadstools—that require organic compounds; and the green plants that need only simple inorganic compounds and light. Among the green plants, the algae are confined to water, and lack differentiated leaves, roots and flowers. The primitive land forms, from mosses up to ferns, have no seeds, and reproduce by microscopic single-celled spores: and the higher land forms, increasingly adapted to land life—including all the familiar trees and flowers—are all seed-plants, with seeds containing an embryo and a store of nutriment. This is, I fear, a tiresome list; but it will at least serve as a reminder of the range of design to be found among the machines for living that we call organisms.

Organisms differ from man's machines in being able to construct themselves. In constructing itself, every

organism goes through a process of individual development—what is technically called its ontogeny. In
primitive forms, this may involve merely minor or
negligible changes, as when a newly formed amoeba
grows to double size before dividing into two. But in all
higher animals and plants, ontogeny is a very elaborate
process, and the developing organism passes through a
whole series of transformations, surprisingly different
in appearance and in mode of working. Every butterfly
was once a caterpillar; every oak once an acorn; every
barnacle once a tiny free-swimming crustacean. You,
like me and every other human being, were once a
microscopic spherical ovum, then in turn a double
sheet of undifferentiated cells, an embryo with enormous outgrowths enabling you to obtain food and
oxygen parasitically from your mother, a creature with
an unjointed rod—what biologists call the notochord—
in place of jointed backbone; you once had gill-clefts
like a fish, you once had a tail, and once were covered
with dense hair like a monkey; you were once a helpless
infant which had to learn to distinguish objects and to
talk; you underwent the transformation of your body
and mind that we call puberty; you learned a job. You
are in fact a self-transforming process.

Ontogeny is thus a pattern of processes in time,
through which the inherent potentialities of the
individual can be realized. Unfavourable conditions
may prevent their full realization, or indeed, by killing
the unfinished individual, prevent any realization at
all; but in favourable conditions development proceeds
freely to the bounds set by its inherent possibilities.
Not only that, but in every generation ontogeny is the
necessary mechanism for realizing the potentialities of
heredity; any new transformation must operate through
the framework of developmental processes which are
available. Organisms tend to resemble each other more
in the earlier than in the later stages of ontogeny. The

THE PROCESS OF EVOLUTION

vast majority of individual plants and animals, however different when adult, resemble each other at the
start of their ontogeny by consisting of a single undifferentiated cell; all embryonic vertebrates—birds
and mammals, fish and reptiles—look remarkably
alike when in the notochord phase of their development; and anyone but a specialist would be hard put
to it to tell rabbits from men, giraffes, or whales even
in much later embryonic stages.

Here let me say a word on recapitulation (Fig. 1 (A),
p. 16). According to Haeckel's theory, ontogeny re-
capitulates phylogeny; in other words, individual
development tends to recapitulate evolutionary
development. This is not strictly true; the individual
does not run through the *adult* stages of its evolutionary
ancestors. What it often does do is to pass through
ancestral developmental stages. The gill-clefts of the
human embryo correspond with those of the fish
embryo, in which they persist (with some slight transformation), to become the gill-slits of the adult fish.
The crinoids (sea-lilies), relatives of the starfish and
sea-urchins, are fixed to the bottom by a stalk as adults.
The feather-star crinoid *Antedon* has no stalk when
adult, and moves about freely, but has a stalked juvenile
phase. The young stages of other crinoids have not yet
been found; but it is an obvious deduction that they
will prove to be stalked, and that *Antedon* is derived
from an ancestor which was stalked both as adult and
young. Thus ontogeny does not actually recapitulate
phylogeny, but may reveal it: it may recapitulate an
ancestral plan of structure.

The asymmetrical sole and other flat-fish reveal
their ancestral bilaterality by passing through a sym-
metrical upright swimming stage before settling down
on one side, and having both their eyes grow round to
the other.

Sometimes the revelation is spectacular. Sea-squirts

(Ascidians) are fixed sessile filter-feeders, with two siphons for taking in and expelling water. They lack nerve-cord and sense-organs, and were for a time classed with clams and similar molluscs. Then, in the 1870's, the Russian zoologist Kovalevsky discovered their larva—a little free-swimming creature with tail and notochord-rod (precursor of the backbone), a nerve-cord along the back, primitive hollow brain-vesicle, eye-spots, gill-clefts; its ground-plan is revealed as similar to that of an embryonic vertebrate, but with no resemblance to the ground-plan of any other group.

Plants may show similar phenomena. As everyone knows, flowering plants develop pollen as their male element. When a pollen-grain comes into contact with the stigma or receptive female part of the flower, it sends out a long pollen-tube which grows until it comes in contact with the ovule. Down the pollen-tube travels a male nucleus, which eventually fertilizes the ovum. In the Maidenhair tree or Gingko (a primitive form which survived only in temple-enclosures in China, though it is now used as an ornamental tree in the streets of cities like New York), the process is similar, except that round the male nucleus there develops a corkscrew-shaped spermatozoon, very similar to the sperms of some ferns and mosses, which swims actively down the microscopic pollen-tube. In ferns and mosses, fertilization requires a film of water in which the sperms can swim freely. The pollen-tube is an arrangement by which fertilization can take place in dry conditions. But though the Gingko is thus fully emancipated from water, its sperms are a reminiscence of a long-previous stage in its evolution.

If we regard recapitulation as a theory implying that phylogeny in some way causes ontogeny, that adult ancestral stages are automatically pressed back into the individual development of later descendants, it is un-true. But if we use it as in a purely descriptive sense, implying no more than that ancestral plans of structure may be retained in development, and so may shed light on evolution and even reveal unexpected relationships, then it is a legitimate and useful term.

Organisms can not only construct themselves, they can also reproduce themselves. One of the most important advances of nineteenth-century biology was the discovery of the physical basis of reproduction. The answer was simple—reproduction depends on continuity of substance. New individuals develop from portions of the living substance of other individuals. The original individual may simply split into two; or it may detach a portion of its substance to serve as a basis for the new individual's development. Even in very large organisms, the detached portions may be only microscopic single cells, as in the spores of plants. In sexual reproduction, two such detached cells, the sperm and the ovum, fuse to form one. But in every case, there is a continuity of living substance, a reproductive stream of life flowing down the generations.

The ancients thought that all kinds of animals, from maggots to mice, could be reproduced *de novo*, by putrefaction, out of slime, and so forth. Later, when the microscope revealed minute creatures like infusoria and bacteria, and it was found that they appeared apparently out of nowhere in infusions and decaying matter, it was natural to suppose that they were generated by the process of decay. However, we now know that it is the bacteria which cause the decay, and not vice versa. The work of Pasteur and his successors has made it clear that life is not now being spontaneously generated.

This at once raises the problem of the first origin of life. To start with, "life" is not a thing, a separate entity. It is a word used to describe the properties and activities of living substance, as observed in animals and plants; and their basic distinguishing property is

23

their capacity for self-reproduction. It in turn appears to be linked with complex chemical molecules, in which nucleic acid is combined with a protein. But many other organic substances, from enzymes to carbohydrates, must be present in the semi-liquid protoplasm.

Even here, it is difficult to draw sharp boundaries. It is hard to see how crystals can be fully alive; yet some plant viruses can be crystallized out in pure form. It has been suggested that they are nucleoproteins which have escaped from an independent organism, and now reproduce themselves by taking advantage of the metabolism of other organisms. Alternatively, they may represent an extreme of degenerative parasitism. In any case, the study of viruses, these tiniest of creatures, is shedding much light on the elementary properties of self-reproducing substance.

There are only three possible alternatives as regards the origin of living substance on this earth. Either it was supernaturally created: or it was brought to the earth from some other place in the universe, in the interior of a meteorite: or it was produced naturally out of less complicated substances.

The first suggestion runs counter to the whole of our scientific knowledge. Living substance consists of the same matter as lifeless substance: it transacts its operations according to the same general rules. There is no trace of any special "vital force" which can be detected or measured. Both the inorganic and the organic world are built out of the same matter, and work by means of the same energy. To postulate a divine interference with these exchanges of matter and energy at a particular moment in the earth's history is both unnecessary and illogical. It is as illogical as it would be to postulate divine interference at each act of fertilization of an ovum by a sperm.

The second alternative presents many technical

difficulties: it is very unlikely that any living substance could survive inside a meteorite. But in any event, it only removes the problem one step further back: we still have to face the question of how this supposed extra-terrestrial life originated.

The third alternative, that living substance evolved out of non-living, is the only hypothesis consistent with scientific continuity. The fact that spontaneous generation does not occur now is no evidence that it did not do so at some earlier stage in the development of this planet, when conditions in the cosmic test-tube were extremely different. Above all, bacteria were not then present, ready to break down any complex substance as soon as formed.

Complex organic molecules are only possible through the property possessed by carbon of linking its atoms in series, to form long chains or rings or ladders. The separate carbon links may have different side-chains attached to them, so that an immense variety of chemical construction is possible. Once conditions had begun to favour the building up of such structures, we may picture the warm shallow seas of the primeval world as so many alembics, teeming with different kinds of carbon chains, the different kinds interacting with each other to form new combinations, a veritable soup of organic compounds. And when one combination arose which was able to utilize others to build up more substance like itself, it would be provided with an enormous reserve of raw materials on which it could draw while refining and perfecting its self-reproductive machinery.

It must be confessed, however, that the actual process is still conjectural; all we know is that living substance must have developed soon after the first rocks of the geological series were laid down, and that this was somewhere about two thousand million years ago. We can be reasonably sure that a relatively simple nucleoprotein marked a crucial stage in the process, and that the earliest truly living things were nothing so elaborate as cells, but more in the nature of naked genes.

In the twentieth century, an even more important advance was made—the detailed mechanism of life's reproductive continuity was discovered, in the shape of the outfit of genes within the chromosomes. This is not the place to expound the principles of genetics. Suffice it to say that a *gene* is the name we use to denote a self-reproducing or self-copying unit of living substance, and that in all groups of animals and plants, with a very few possible exceptions among the lowest forms, but including bacteria, the genetic outfit is of the same general nature, consisting of a definite and large number of different genes, arranged in a definite linear order within a much smaller number of the visible cell-organs called chromosomes. Each particular kind of gene can exist in a number of slightly different forms or "allels," each allel exerting a slightly different effect in development. The genetic outfit is typically double, one whole set or pack of genes and chromosomes from the father and one from the mother. Under the microscope, you can see the strange and beautiful figures which the chromosomes execute to ensure the proper distribution of the genes. During the growth of cells capable of further division, the genes reproduce or copy themselves, so that they and the chromosomes come to exist in closely apposed identical pairs: and at each ordinary cell-division the two halves of each pair are pulled apart from each other, giving the appearance of chromosome-splitting. This ensures that each cell receives an entire double genetic outfit (Fig. 1 (B), p. 16).

Before sexual reproduction, a more complicated set of manœuvres takes place, by means of which the maternal and paternal outfits are shuffled and redealt in new ways. Each reproductive cell—sperm or egg—contains one entire outfit, but each has a different assortment of maternal and paternal genes; through their union at fertilization, each offspring reacquires a double pack, but each such duplex set contains a different combination of allels: that is why no two individuals (except identical twins) are genetically alike. This is the genetic process of *recombination*, which is one of the major sources of life's variability. Only with a definite linear arrangement of genes can you secure continuity of reproduction and constancy of composition; only with sexual recombination can you secure adequate variability.

There is one more basic fact common to all life. Genes are very complicated things—a single gene contains many thousands of atoms, organized in a definite pattern and arrangement. Because of this complexity, the process of self-reproduction is not always quite accurate: the copy occasionally differs from the original in some slight respect. This incomplete self-copying of genes is called their *mutation*. The mutated gene then continues to reproduce itself in its new form. As is to be expected on general theoretical grounds, mutation takes place in all organisms that have been studied, and apparently in all their genes, within a certain range of low frequency. Wherever one kind of gene exists in the form of two different allels, one of them is the result of a prior mutation. Whereas the sexual process provides new variation in the shape of combinations of old mutants, mutation provides wholly new substantive variations.

The relative position of the genes can be mapped by discovering the closeness of their linkage; and in *Drosophila*, this genetic map can be related to the map of visible structure as revealed by the microscope in the giant chromosomes of the salivary glands. Genetic

27

geography is linear, and you can point to the exact position of a gene along the length of a particular chromosome.

The genetic outfit is built on this general plan in all organisms from bacteria to men, though the details can be modified during evolution. An obvious modification, found in various plants, is what is called polyploidy—the multiplication of the number of chromosome-sets.

The total number of genes is much greater than originally supposed. The best estimate naturally comes from *Drosophila*, which probably boasts about 5000. Five thousand genes in a tiny fly, all different, and each containing thousands of atoms! It is a salutary reminder of the complexity of life.

Though the genes behave as separable units in heredity, they interact during development. Physiologically, they constitute a single system, the integrated gene-complex.

The gene-complex exerts its effects through the mechanism of individual development. There is always a longer or shorter chain of processes intervening between the genes in the chromosomes and the characters of the functioning animal or plant. Unfortunately, the precise way genes act during development is still very imperfectly understood. But here and there, we are getting some insight. In the first place, there is no one-to-one correspondence between genes and characters. At least a dozen main genes, and probably many minor ones, are concerned with normal mouse colouration, and before they get to work, many others must have been busy shaping the hairs, the structure of the skin and so forth. In general, many genes influence any single character. Sometimes so-called multiple genes, with similar and supplementary effects, are at work, as with red versus white grain-colour in wheat.

Conversely, one gene may affect several characters.

One mutant gene in *Drosophila* changes the eye from red to white, alters the pigmentation of the male testis, and changes the shape of the female spermatheca.

Then the expression of genes may be altered by environmental factors. So-called Himalayan rabbits are partial albinos, with black ears and feet. The extremities are at a slightly lower temperature than the rest of the body, and here the "Himalayan" gene can build up black pigment. If white fur is plucked from the body and the animal kept cold, the new fur grows black. The Himalayan pattern is the result of an interaction between a particular gene and particular conditions of temperature.

Some genes directly affect the rate of a process. In the shrimp *Gammarus* the difference between red and black eyes in the adult is due to a gene altering the rate at which black melanin pigment is deposited.

Other genes affect timing. The so-called creeper mutant in fowls, with short thick legs and extremely reduced wings, depends on a gene which brings about a general retardation of development at the 36th hour of incubation. The organs which are growing most rapidly at that time are most affected, in this case the wings.

Some genetic differences act as a switch mechanism, turning on a whole battery of further processes. An obvious case is that of sex in *Drosophila* and ourselves. Here sex is determined by the so-called X-chromosomes —two for a female, one for a male. This primary difference then switches on one of the two alternative modes of sexual development, with all their differences in primary and secondary sex-characters.

We can look at the matter from the angle of development. How do developmental processes canalize the action of genes? I cannot embark on the enormous subject of experimental embryology, and must confine myself to a couple of examples. Gradients exist in the developing organism—gradients in metabolism, growth-potential, and other factors. Genes altering the shape and intensity of such gradients will affect a number of parts simultaneously. Thus the proportions of the digits in a vertebrate limb seem to depend on gradients affecting rate of differentiation and, later, relative growth. The difference in shape between a flat snail-shell like *Planorbis* and the pointed spiral cone of a tower-shell depends primarily on a simple difference in the growth-gradients of the shell-forming mantle-edge.

Again, in higher vertebrates, hormones may affect a large number of processes. The sex-hormones influence all the various sexual characters: the anterior pituitary affects many processes of growth in a co-ordinated way. Genes concerned with such mechanisms may obviously have evolutionary consequences.

In general, the importance of individual development for evolution lies in the fact that it provides the framework through which changes in genes must express themselves. In the long run, the genes control development; in the short run, development influences the genes' mode of action.

Striking evolutionary effects can be expected when the general tempo of differentiation is speeded up or slowed down, or one phase of development prolonged into another, as Dr. de Beer has shown in his *Embryos and Ancestors*. Thus the slowing down of the thyroid gland's growth, and the delaying of the moment when it liberates its secretion, has given us the Mexican axolotl. This is a salamander tadpole which never metamorphoses into a land animal, but becomes sexually mature in the gill-breathing larval form. A simple meal of thyroid will reconvert it into a land salamander.

It has been suggested with some plausibility that insects were derived from myriapods by a somewhat similar process. The newly hatched myriapod has only three pairs of legs instead of a whole series all down the body. If this stage were prolonged until sexual maturity, the adult "thousand-leg" phase would drop out of existence, and you would have a creature very like a primitive insect.

Again, much of the difference between man and apes seems to be due to the slowing of differentiation in man, who thus in many respects resembles a foetal ape. This retardation will of course not account for all distinctive human features, but it was a necessary pre-requisite for their full evolution.

But I am straying from my main subject.

To complete my rapid outline picture of biological evolution, I must make it four-dimensional by extending it in time. We now have a quantitative scale of geological time, based on dating by means of radio-active minerals, which is accurate to within about ten per cent. Life came into being some two thousand million years ago. At longish intervals, the earth went through periods of mountain-building, the last of which threw up all the existing great ranges—all destined to be worn down and flattened out by erosion and denudation in the further course of geological time. The geographical and climatic changes resulting from these geological revolutions affected the evolution of life in a number of ways.

For the biologist who wants to study the time-relations of evolution, fossils are the basic documents. The facts of comparative anatomy and ontogeny, of adaptation and geographical distribution and ecology, all shed essential light on the process; but fossil remains provide direct evidence. Unfortunately, for perhaps three-quarters of geological time, the rocks are almost bare of them: any that there were have mostly been baked or squashed out of recognition, while most animals could not get fossilized at all, as they were still soft-bodied. Fossils first became abundant rather over five hundred million years ago. The time since then is divided into three main epochs of decreasing length—the Paleozoic, or Age of Ancient Life, which lasted just over three hundred million years; the Mesozoic, or Age of Intermediate Life, of about a hundred and thirty-five million years; and the Cenozoic, or Age of Modern Life, of about sixty-five million. The final period, since the beginning of the last Ice Age, has lasted rather under one million years.

As we go back in time, the forms that were especially abundant in each epoch fail to appear in the fossil record, and quite different creatures are found as dominant types. To take the vertebrates, before about a million years ago we find no men; much earlier, no reptiles, then, earlier again, no land forms at all, but fish as dominant vertebrates; and finally, no vertebrates with jaws or true paired limbs, but only jawless limbless animals related to the lampreys. Among the arthropods, as we travel back, the crabs fade out a little before the mammals, the insects about the same time as the reptiles, while in the early Paleozoic two groups quite unknown from the rocks of later Ages were in the ascendant, the great sea-scorpions and the little creeping trilobites.

Today, thanks to the laborious work of the paleontologists, we can give a quite detailed account of the kind of process that is involved. Wherever abundant fossils provide adequate documentation, we can see that each new dominant type, as it appears, radiates out into a progressively greater variety of lines or sub-types, each adapted to a different way of life. Thus the modern mammals radiated to produce rodents, hoofed animals, whales, carnivores, bats, monkeys, and so on. Not only that, but with few exceptions each line, and each sub-line within it, shows a more or less steady trend or tendency over millions or tens of millions of years, in the direction of closer adaptation to its special way of

Fig. 2. The display of the Argus pheasant: " an apparent improbability produced by selection." (p. 51)

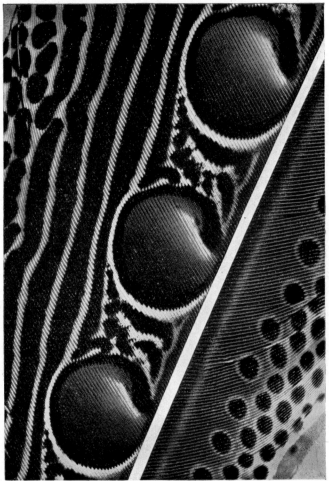

Fig. 3   *W. Suschitzky*

Three ocelli from a male Argus pheasant's wing-feather (p. 51)

life; but it finally becomes stabilized and shows no further major change, merely throwing off new species and other minor variations on the existing theme. The few exceptions give rise to new dominant types, which blossom out in their turn, as did the one line of small nocturnal running reptiles which turned into the mammals. Some stabilized types persist apparently indefinitely, like the lung-fishes, for three hundred million years—or the ants, for perhaps fifty million. Others become wholly extinct, like the trilobites and the sea-scorpions and most of the Mesozoic reptiles.

When we take an instantaneous snapshot, we freeze the process into a set of unreal static pictures. What we need is the equivalent of a film. We all know how a film record can be speeded up to reveal processes that are hidden from ordinary view—the dancing movements of a growing twig, the adventurous transformations of a developing egg. The same applies to our moving picture of evolution. If this is run at what seems natural speed, we see only individual lives and deaths. But when with the aid of our scientific knowledge and our imagination we alter the time-scale of our vision, new processes become apparent. With a hundred-fold speeding up, individual lives become merged in the formation and transformation of species. With our film speeded up perhaps ten thousand times single species disappear, and group-radiations are revealed; we see an original type, seized by a ferment of activity, splitting up and transforming itself in many strange ways, but all the transformations eventually slowing down and stabilizing in specialized immobility. Only in the longest perspective, with a hundred-thousand-fold speed-up, do the overall processes of evolution become visible—the replacement of old types by new, the emergence and gradual liberation of mind, the narrow and winding stairway of progress, and the steady advance of life up its steps of novelty.

Let me give just three examples of biological novelties and their effects. The first is a quantitative novelty—the evolution, undoubtedly after hundreds of millions of years of single-celled and therefore microscopic life, of many-celled and therefore potentially much larger organisms. This opened the door to an increase in complexity of organization and to all kinds of qualitative novelties such as glands, eyes, blood-systems and brains. The second is the evolution of temperature-regulation or "warm-bloodedness." This took place only within the last tenth of evolutionary time, and only in birds and mammals. It could not have done so earlier, but once it had been achieved, it formed the necessary basis for the further improvement of mental properties which made possible the evolution of man. The third is the appearance of colour in the world, which depended on the evolution of eyes capable of seeing coloured patterns. Only the vertebrates, the cuttlefish and their relatives, and the higher arthropods (like insects and spiders) have eyes capable of seeing a pattern, and so detecting the shape, size and movement of objects; and some of these have eyes capable of seeing that pattern in colour. We do not know just when coloured pattern-vision was first evolved; certainly not until quite late on in evolutionary time. But once evolved, it had remarkable effects. It led to the evolution of patterns and colours with biological significance in an enormous range of organisms, plants as well as animals, from insect-pollinated flowers to courting birds. It generated protective colouration and aggressive bluff, and was the first if not the only be-getter of beauty (Figs. 2 and 3, pp. 32 and 33).

I am tempted to add a fourth example—the evolution of those particular organizations of knowledge which we call concepts. This went hand-in-hand with the evolution of language—the invention of words as symbols for things, in place of sounds as signs for feelings, and was made possible by the expansion of the association areas in the cerebral cortex of the first ancestral men. "In the beginning was the Word" is true of the development of human culture, for the evolution of verbal concepts opened the door to all further organizations and achievements of man's thought.

Newton clarified the whole of physical science and made the universe more comprehensible by introducing a few simple principles and postulates, such as the laws of motion, the postulate that matter consisted of uniform particles, the law of inverse squares governing their attraction; and then calculating and checking their implications. Thanks to Darwin and the Darwinians and then to Mendel and the Mendelians, the time is approaching when we can hope to do the same sort of thing for biology. Here the simple principles (of course based on an enormous volume of ascertained fact) are that the basis of life's continuity consists of incompletely self-copying genes, and that the natural selection which results from this primary fact is the essential agency in causing evolution to happen as it does. A further necessary postulate is that there are mental as well as material properties of the universe; that mental properties can be of biological advantage to their possessors; and that they become more important and more intense in the special and highly organized systems we call brains. Just as the movements of planets and the path of projectiles could be understood on the basis of the Newtonian postulates and principles, so we are beginning to see how we might understand the trends of evolution, from adaptation to broad improvement, from the origin of species to the succession of major groups, on the basis of Darwinian-Mendelian postulates and principles.

Today we can see life as a unitary process, made up of a number of smaller processes. The individual organism is a process within the species, the species a process within the radiation of a type, the radiation of a type a process within the succession of dominant groups, and this in turn a process within the overall process of realizing new possibilities of variety and organization. And this point of view suggests questions of a new sort—questions about the nature and form of evolutionary processes, their definition and measurement, their limitations and restriction; questions about potentialities and their realization, about higher and lower, about improvement and progress. Above all, we have to ask how we can come to terms scientifically with a reality which combines both material and mental properties in its unitary pattern. Biology is much more complex than mechanics or physics. So it will be a long time before we can devise satisfactory methods for answering such questions, and can work out in detail the implications of such postulates and principles, especially their quantitative ones. But that does not prevent it being necessary to ask the new questions: that is the way in which scientific comprehension advances.

The next step will be to discover just how historical or evolutionary processes operate, and to organize our knowledge about them in satisfactory formulations. This will involve a new approach, different from that of much of present-day science. We may call it the pattern-process approach, for it has to deal with the development, in time, of elaborate structural and functional patterns of organization. It will eventually lead to a science of developmental pattern. Like any other step in scientific or any other kind of thinking, it too will certainly be limited, and will not give us either complete or absolute knowledge. But it should get us out of the impasse into which a predominantly static and analytic approach has been leading us; it should free us from the bogy of causal determinism; and it should be able to serve as the basis for as yet undreamt-of further steps in thought.

One thing it is doing: it is already leading us towards a new and momentous answer to the old riddle of human destiny. In broad terms, the destiny of man on earth has been made clear by evolutionary biology. It is to be the agent of the world process of evolution, the sole agent capable of leading it to new heights, and enabling it to realize new possibilities. But this is to anticipate the rest of this little book.

NOTE

In calling evolution irreversible, I was referring to the process as a whole. In the inorganic sector, there are of course many small-scale and short-range changes which are fully reversible. In biology, some aspects of individual development are reversible. Thus planarian worms can be made to "de-grow" by starvation, and then fed again to restore their former age, size and proportions. This, however, is a reversal of a single stage of development only; and development seems to be irreversible when it involves a complex sequence of stages.

When we come to genetics, we find that the process of mutation is itself frequently reversible, a mutant gene being capable of mutating back to "normal."

Some true evolutionary changes seem to be reversible. For instance, in some lines of horses, the general trend to increase of size has been reversed, and the animals have become somewhat smaller. However, it is almost inconceivable that the end-result would depend on the same set of size-determining genes as in the original small-sized form. No case is known where a broad trend involving many characters has been fully reversed. Thus all terrestrial animals which have become secondarily adapted to aquatic life, like the whales or the ichthyosaurs, retain many evidences of their stay on land.

To sum up, we may say that, though organs once evolved may be reduced or lost, and sometimes small reversals of trend may occur, long-term and large-scale evolution is truly irreversible.

CHAPTER II

How Natural Selection Works

In my first chapter I tried to give some idea of the variety manifested by life during its evolution. Now I must dig down in an attempt to discover its unity. There are two key concepts or principles at our disposal. One, as we have known ever since the time of Darwin, is natural selection; the other, as we are now beginning to realize, is biological improvement. Natural selection is the guiding force, and biological improvement is the general term for the resultant positive trends. Natural selection, be it noted, can also act as a stabilizing force in certain conditions.

The two principles can be stated in the form of two general evolutionary equations. The first is that reproduction plus mutation produces natural selection; and the second that natural selection plus time produces the various degrees of biological improvement that we find in nature. Both result from a single property of all living matter—its property of copying itself, but with occasional inaccuracies.

The process of self-copying results in reproduction; reproduction results in more offspring being produced than can survive to reproduce again; and this in turn results in what Darwin called the struggle for existence. Mutation is the result of occasional inaccuracies in the various parts of the hereditary constitution, down to the ultimate units we call genes—failures to maintain some detail of their complicated physical and chemical structure; and these inaccuracies are then faithfully reproduced by the self-copying process, so that the original mutation becomes a strain of mutant genes. If self-copying serves as the basis of continuity and specificity in life, and reproduction generates its expansive force, mutation is the ultimate source of all its heritable variation. Variations inevitably differ in the degree of biological advantage they confer—in other words, their survival value; and so the struggle for existence results in their differential survival—in other words, natural selection. Advantageous or favourable variations will be gradually bred into the stock, the disadvantageous or unfavourable ones gradually bred out.

Of course the struggle for existence and natural selection are both highly metaphorical terms. "The struggle for existence" merely signifies that a portion of each generation is bound to die before it can reproduce itself; while "natural selection" is a convenient shorthand phrase for the differential survival and reproduction of variants, and its effects in each generation. For instance, if two variants are present in equal numbers in a population, and one has a selective advantage of four per cent. over the other, the proportion of the two in the next generation will be shifted by natural selection from fifty-fifty to about fifty-one to forty-nine. Actually, this would be a high degree of selective advantage, and in point of fact one much smaller, down to one-half of one per cent. or even lower, though you could never detect it in nature, would be effective in gradually transforming a species.

So far, we have been considering what happens between single generations of single species. It remains to extend the argument both in time and in space, to cover the long succession of generations in the process of life as a whole. Darwin essayed this, too: in Chapter 4 of the *Origin* he wrote that "the ultimate result of natural selection is that each creature tends to become more and more improved in relation to its conditions. This improvement inevitably leads to the gradual advancement of the organization of the greater number of living beings." But he never pursued this part of his argument to its logical conclusion. However, he did realize that natural selection must in the long run result in something that deserves to be called "improvement" and in so doing provided us with a key concept in this larger sphere.

The discovery of the principle of natural selection made evolution comprehensible; together with the discoveries of modern genetics, it has rendered all other explanations of evolution untenable. So far as we now know, not only is natural selection inevitable, not only is it *an* effective agency of evolution, but it is *the* only effective agency of evolution. With the knowledge that has been amassed since Darwin's time, it is no longer possible to believe that evolution is brought about through the so-called inheritance of acquired characters —the direct effects of use or disuse of organs, or of changes in the environment; or by the conscious or unconscious will of organisms; or through the operation of some mysterious vital force; or by any other inherent tendency. What this means, in the technical terms of biology, is that all the theories lumped together under the heads of orthogenesis and Lamarckism are invalidated, including Lysenko's Michurinism, which is now the officially approved theory of genetics and evolution in the U.S.S.R. They are "out": they are no longer consistent with the facts. Indeed, in the light of modern discoveries, they no longer deserve to be called scientific theories, but can be seen as speculations without due basis of reality, or old superstitions disguised in modern dress. They were natural enough in their time, when we were still ignorant of the mechanism of heredity; but they have now only a historical interest.

Sometimes the inheritance of acquired characters is simulated. Thus all our tendons are adapted to their function, both in size and strength and direction. But these detailed adaptations seem all to be due to a single property of the fibre-forming tissue from which they arise. The cells orient themselves along lines of tension, and multiply faster here than elsewhere. All that is inherited is a general adaptation of fibroblast tissue to respond to the demands upon it: the detailed adaptations are secondary non-inherited modifications, produced anew by use in each generation. This takes a heavy burden off the shoulders of natural selection, which is not involved except in regard to the basic capacity to react. The same sort of thing seems to hold for the fine architecture of our bones, which becomes beautifully adjusted during development to the mechanical stresses and strains acting upon it.

Lamarckism may also be simulated by what Baldwin and Lloyd-Morgan called organic selection. By this they meant that mere modifications of behaviour may adjust an animal to a new environment long enough for mutations in the same direction to arise and be selected for. When Thorpe reared *Drosophila* grubs on media flavoured with peppermint, the adults were attracted by the same smell to lay their eggs. Such "olfactory conditioning" could readily operate when an insect takes to a new food-plant, and could then lead on to genetic adaptations.

I am afraid this all sounds rather dry and abstract. But, actually, the idea of natural selection, once it has been properly grasped with all its implications, is extremely illuminating, enabling one to see the phenomena of life in a new and exciting way. Most basically, natural selection converts accident into apparent design, randomness into organized pattern. Mutation merely provides the raw material of evolution; it is a random affair, and takes place in all directions. Genes are giant molecules, and their mutations are the result of slight alterations in their structure. Some of these alterations are truly chance rearrangements, as uncaused or at least as unpredictable as the jumping of an electron from one orbit to another inside an atom; others are the result of the impact of some external agency, like X-rays, or ultra-violet radiations, or mustard gas. But in all cases they are random in relation to evolution. Their effects are not related to the needs of the organism, or to the conditions in which it is placed. They occur without reference to their possible consequences or biological uses. It is true that we sometimes find "pre-adaptation" to some other environment; but that is a very different matter. Thus a mutant strain of water-flea was found to be adapted to a temperature $7°C$ above the optimum for the parent type. A mutation in tobacco prevented the plants from flowering in the latitude of Washington, where it originated, but was pre-adapted to more tropical regions.

To put the matter in a nutshell: the capacity of living substance for reproduction is the expansive driving force of evolution; mutation provides its raw material; but natural selection determines its direction.

One would expect that any interference with such a complicated piece of chemical machinery as the genetic constitution would result in damage. And in fact this is so: the great majority of mutant genes are harmful in their effects on the organism. A few have favourable effects, or effects that can become favourable in combination with other genes. Selection automatically incorporates this tiny minority of favourable variations into the hereditary constitution, by sifting them from the mass of unusable dross. Of course, selection also actively weeds out the unfavourable variations—the most harmful ones immediately, the less harmful after a greater or lesser number of generations. Mutations repeat themselves with a certain frequency. So, if this weeding-out process did not occur, a harmful mutant, like haemophilia (or bleeding) in man, would gradually grow more and more abundant. Thus selection is necessary merely to maintain the biological efficiency of animal and plant species. In the absence of this maintenance selection, as we may call it, harmful mutations are not weeded out; they accumulate, and genetic degeneration sets in. This is what has happened in various species of cave fish, for example: in caves there was no selection for efficiency of vision, and their eyes have degenerated, sometimes to total disappearance. It should be noted that cave animals are derived mainly from types which shun light and often have poorly developed eyes. So here constitutional pre-adaptation may lead on to genetic degeneration. Selection thus acts in three main ways. It determines the direction of new positive evolutionary change or improvement; it maintains the level of existing improvement; and its absence leads to "disimprovement" or degeneration.[1]

We can sometimes actually see selection in action. Let me give a few examples. Everyone knows that some diseases can be successfully treated with drugs that kill the bacteria causing them. But sometimes treatment of this sort, instead of killing the bacteria, produces a resistant strain. The American biologist Demerec grew the bacterium called *Escherischia coli* in cultures containing the bactericidal drug streptomycin. It soon became totally resistant to any reasonable dose. This, he found, was not due to all the bacteria becoming gradually more and more resistant, but to the presence in every large culture (which may run to tens or hundreds of thousands of millions of individuals) of a few mutants which have already mutated, quite irrelevantly and accidentally, in such a way as to be able to resist the action of streptomycin. The important

---

[1] This process will be very much slower when sexual recombination has been abandoned. In such cases one would expect to find "relict adaptations" in structures originally evolved to secure sexual cross-fertilization. This may account for the persistence of showy flower-heads in dandelions, although they now reproduce wholly non-sexually and do not require the visits of insects.

43

point is that the mutants were there already: the mutations which gave rise to them took place long before the streptomycin treatment was started. But once it was started, they alone could survive and multiply: all the rest, other mutants as well as normals, died off.[1]

On the other hand, *Staphylococcus aureus* required four or five mutational steps to develop full resistance to penicillin. Here presumably new mutations were involved in the later steps, in addition to the selection of pre-existent mutants. But the entire process depended on selection.

The same appears to hold for the scale insects infesting citrus crops in California. Over the past half-century they have become progressively more resistant to the deadly poison, hydrocyanic acid. Fumigation dosage had to be stepped up; firms no longer guaranteed success; spraying had to be introduced; and the increased spray dosage began to damage the trees. Here too selection was a matter of life and death, and the resultant change was much faster than anything to be expected in nature.

Next, an experimental demonstration of selection. The insects called water-boatmen vary in colour and shade. When samples of these were put in vessels with different shades of background, each with an insect-

---

[1] Recently, Hinshelwood has produced evidence that in some bacteria, culturing them in solutions of different sugars will actually give rise to new types, which can utilize the new kind of nutriment by means of a change in the enzymes they produce. It remains to be seen whether these changes are of the same nature as the gene-mutations of higher organisms, or (as is more probable) enzyme-adaptations due to reversible changes in the general protoplasm, a result of the fact that bacteria stand in a more direct relation with their chemical environment.

It is certainly true that the genes of higher organisms are carefully preserved from the direct influence of many chemical changes, by being enclosed in a selective nuclear membrane, and the nucleus in its turn within a selective cell-membrane. Furthermore, when a mutation is artificially produced, it will affect only one of the two members of a pair of genes within a single cell, showing that mutation is an exceedingly local effect, not the result of some general change in conditions.

eating fish in it, the ones which were conspicuous by differing from the background were eaten in greater numbers. The greater the conspicuousness, and the smaller the total number of water-boatmen, the greater was the selective disadvantage—in some cases up to five of the more conspicuous were eaten for every one of the inconspicuous.

Next, a diagrammatically simple case. In poultry, there is a mutation called frizzled. This acts so as to set the feathers up on end and allow the body-heat to escape, so that frizzled fowls cannot be kept alive in Britain through the year, except in heated rooms. But in the tropics they can exist perfectly well, and in some places strains with frizzled feathers do better than breeds with normal ones. The frizzled mutant is thus at a high selective disadvantage in cold climates, at a slight selective advantage in hot ones.

Then there is the remarkable case of what is called industrial melanism—the fact that during the past hundred years many different species of moths have become virtually black in industrial towns, while remaining light and protectively coloured in the countryside. In these species, the melanics, or dark forms, are much hardier than the normals, but these— the light ones—are better concealed from their enemies in the unblackened countryside. So they have a selective advantage there, while the melanics are better able to resist the smoke and contamination of the industrial areas. Here, again, the new conditions had nothing whatever to do with the origin of the mutation which results in melanism. There were always a few rare melanics—much valued, incidentally, by collectors— and the new conditions merely provided them with their opportunity.[1]

[1] This only applies to dominant melanics. Recessive melanics are never hardier than normals and have not given rise to any industrial melanic forms.

Finally, we have the curious fact that the harmful effects of mutant genes may automatically be selected back towards normality. For instance, the so-called eyeless mutant of the famous fruit-fly, *Drosophila*, at its first appearance had no or small eyes, and was less healthy and in general less capable of survival than normal wild-type flies. But after a pure eyeless strain had been bred for eight or ten generations, both its health and vigour and its eyes were almost normal. Any odd mutant genes already present in small numbers in the strain, which reduced the harmful effects of the eyeless mutation, automatically multiplied at the expense of those which did not. Natural selection, in fact, provided a genetic servo-mechanism to regulate the mutant back towards normality in its effects.

"That is all very well," you may say. "It seems to be true that natural selection can turn moths black in industrial areas, can keep protective colouration up to the mark, can produce resistant strains of bacteria and insect pests. But what about really elaborate improvements? Can it transform a reptile's leg into a bird's wing, or turn a monkey into a man? How can a blind and automatic sifting process like selection, operating on a blind and undirected process like mutation, produce organs like the eye or the brain, with their almost incredible complexity and delicacy of adjustment? How can chance produce elaborate design? In a word, are you not asking us to believe too much?" The answer is no: all this is not too much to believe, once one has grasped the way the process operates. Professor R. A. Fisher once summed the matter up in a pithy phrase—"Natural selection is a mechanism for generating an exceedingly high degree of improbability." Of course, this is in a sense a paradox, and the improbability is only an apparent one: but it is a useful short-hand phrase to denote the real improbability of the results having been produced in any other way than by means of natural selection. The clue to the paradox is time. The longer selection operates, the more improbable (in this sense) are its results; and in point of fact it has been operating for a very long time indeed. All living things are equally old—they can all trace their ancestry back some two thousand million years. With that length of time available, little adjustments can easily be made to add up to miraculous adaptations; and the slight shifts of gene-frequency between one generation and the next can be multiplied to produce radical improvements and totally new kinds of creatures.

A little calculation demonstrates how incredibly improbable the results of natural selection can be when enough time is available. Following Professor Muller, we can ask what would have been the odds against a higher animal, such as a horse, being produced by chance alone: that is to say by the accidental accumulation of the necessary favourable mutations, *without* the intervention of selection. To calculate these odds, we need to estimate two quantities—the proportion of favourable mutations to useless or harmful ones; and the total number of mutational steps, or successive favourable mutations, needed for the production of a horse from some simple microscopic ancestor. A proportion of favourable mutations of one in a thousand does not sound much, but is probably generous, since so many mutations are lethal, preventing the organism living at all, and the great majority of the rest throw the machinery slightly out of gear. And a total of a million mutational steps sounds a great deal, but is probably an under-estimate—after all, that only means one step every two thousand years during biological time as a whole. However, let us take these figures as being reasonable estimates. With this proportion, but without any selection, we should clearly have to breed a thousand strains to get one with one favourable mutation; a million strains (a thousand squared) to get one containing two favourable mutations; and so on, up to a thousand to the millionth power to get one containing a million.

Of course, this could not really happen, but it is a useful way of visualizing the fantastic odds against getting a number of favourable mutations in one strain through pure chance alone. A thousand to the millionth power, when written out, becomes the figure 1 with three million noughts after it: and that would take three large volumes of about five hundred pages each, just to print! Actually this is a meaninglessly large figure, but it shows what a degree of improbability natural selection has to surmount, and can circumvent. One with three million noughts after it is the measure of the unlikeliness of a horse—the odds against it happening at all. No one would bet on anything so improbable happening; and yet it *has* happened. It has happened, thanks to the workings of natural selection and the properties of living substance which make natural selection inevitable.

Let us look at the matter in a more realistic way. What natural selection actually *does* is to take a series of rare and abnormal events, in the shape of favourable mutations, and make them (or strictly speaking, the resultant mutant genes) common and normal. As we have just seen, the proportion of favourable to unfavourable mutations can be taken as one in a thousand. The frequency of mutation itself is much lower. It varies a good deal: for some genes it is as high as one mutation in fifty thousand, for others as low as one in several million. Perhaps we may take an average of one in a hundred thousand—after reproduction has provided a hundred thousand genes, you may expect that one of them will have mutated. So the actual frequency of favourable mutations will average only one in ten million available genes. Nevertheless, once a rare favourable mutation crops up, selection can and does

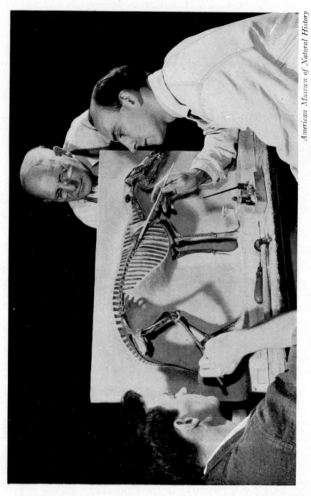

Fig. 4. The earliest known horse (p. 55). A skeleton of Eohippus from Lower Eocene rocks being mounted for exhibition.

convert it, in the course of a mere few hundreds of generations, into a normal character of the group; and so on with the next and the next.

In actual practice, the existence of sex renders the process enormously speedier; for it makes possible the combination of all the mutant genes that already exist in different individuals of a species, as well as those that may crop up at different times during the evolutionary future. Sex is thus an indispensable ally of selection in the business of effecting evolutionary change, for it enormously increases the possibility of securing favourable combinations of mutant genes; and it is no accident that sexual recombination has only been abandoned in forms for which stability is more immediately advantageous than change.

On the basis of our present knowledge, natural selection is bound to produce genetic adaptations: and genetic adaptations are thus presumptive evidence for the efficacy of natural selection.

We have got used to the idea—which was very disturbing when Lyell first advanced it over a hundred years ago—that the "eternal hills" are not eternal at all, but will all eventually be flattened out, while the materials of which they are made will be deposited to make new rocks elsewhere; and that this all takes place by the accumulation, over a very long lapse of time, of the scarcely perceptible changes that are always going on. We are now getting used to the even more disturbing idea that living nature (including our own nature) is not unchangeable, but can be and is moulded into the strangest shapes; and that this takes place by the slow accumulation of the scarcely perceptible changes brought about by natural selection in each generation. In face of this realization, all the objections to a selectionist explanation of evolution that are based on the improbability of its results, simply fall to the ground. In fact the shoe is now on the other foot. Improbability is to be *expected* as the result of natural selection; and we have the paradox that an exceedingly high apparent improbability in its products can be taken as evidence for the high degree of its efficacy.

The efficacy of natural selection can also be gauged by studying the way its effects vary in relation to variations in external conditions. Let me just give one example—the geographical variation in the size of warm-blooded animals. Most small or moderate-sized species of warm-blooded animals—birds and mammals —vary in size with latitude; the nearer polewards they live, the bigger they are. Thus, for each degree of north latitude, the linear dimensions of puffins increase by over one per cent.; with the result that puffins from their furthest north in Spitsbergen have nearly double the bulk of puffins from their furthest south on the coast of Brittany. The biological reason for this is that absolutely larger bodies have a relatively smaller surface, and so lose heat less readily. The regular increase of size with latitude is a delicate adaptation for adjusting the temperature-regulating machinery of the species to the average local temperature: and selection must all the time be operating to maintain the delicacy of this adjustment.

A strange precision of adaptation is seen in whirligig beetles and the fish *Anableps*, which have their eyes divided into two parts, with different refractive indices, the upper for seeing in air, the lower for seeing in water. This seems very peculiar—until we find that they spend most of their time actually in the surface film of still waters.

Even more peculiar is the fact that the giant clam *Tridacna*, whose shells are sometimes used for holy-water stoups, has a number of lenses near the free edge of its mantle, but that these have nothing to do with vision. By concentrating light, they serve to increase the growth and multiplication of the swarms of microscopic algae that live in the clam's tissues. At first sight this seems to contradict the principle laid down by Darwin, that natural selection can never generate anything for the sole benefit of another species. Actually, however, the lenses benefit the clam too, for the relation between it and the algae is a symbiotic one. The algae benefit by the waste nitrogenous products of the clam; but their surplus population is led away by ingenious mechanisms to be digested in the clam's gut. The "improbable" lenses are adaptations to increase this surplus.

Now for just one example of extreme apparent improbability—the enormously elongated wings of the male Argus pheasant, adorned with their marvellously beautiful eye-spots shaded to give the illusion of solidity —a truly astonishing production of nature, as any of you who have seen the bird in a zoo will agree (Figs. 2 and 3, pp. 32 and 33). In display, the wings are thrown forward in the form of a bell directed towards the hen bird. The whole of the rest of the body is concealed; and the wings are never thus shown off except in sexual display. Their structure and pattern and the actions concerned in showing them off would be meaningless unless the display were of biological advantage—in other words, unless it had selective value. Luckily, we know that in this case the intensity of selection is extremely high. Argus pheasants are promiscuously polygamous. A successful male may succeed in mating with half a dozen hens, while some of his less successful rivals may secure no mates at all. The display of the males helps to stimulate the females and induce readiness to mate, so any improvement in its beauty and its stimulating qualities will be at a very high premium.

Passing on from this, we find a very interesting correlation in male birds between the intensity of the selection that is operating on their display and the development of their display characters. In most small monogamous birds, display before the female only begins after the male has paired up for the season. So the utmost advantage it can secure is to stimulate the female to lay a slightly larger clutch of eggs, and to lay them earlier. In correlation with this merely *fractional* reproductive advantage, such displays consist merely in actions like drooping the wings and fanning the tail, without the development of special plumes or patterns adapted to be shown off during the process. But such birds have another sort of display—an advertisement display, by which the males advertise their possession of a breeding territory, proclaiming a warning to rivals, an invitation to potential mates. Here *unit* reproductive success is involved: the more successful males secure and retain a mate, the less successful do not. There is thus a fairly high selective advantage, and in correlation with this the display characters are quite conspicuous— bright patterns or loud songs that can be effective at a distance, like the male yellow-hammer's bright colours, or the nightingale's song. Finally, in polygamous species there is the possibility of *multiple* reproductive success— one male may secure many mates. An exceedingly high selection-pressure comes into play, and as a result the characters directly involved in display before the female may be exaggerated to the limit. Indeed, the Argus pheasant's wings, however useful for reproductive success, are so hypertrophied that they must be an actual handicap in the ordinary business of living.

This leads on to yet another interesting point—that natural selection need not always benefit the species. This is so when it is the result merely of intra-specific competition—in other words, when the competition for survival or reproduction is entirely between different individuals within the species. Thus when the prize of individual success in reproduction is as great as with male Argus pheasants, selection may even operate so as to reduce the individual's chances in other aspects of existence. The result is an equilibrium—a compromise between different advantages.

Sometimes selection for one character will have consequential effects on others. Many organs, like deer antlers or the jaws of male stag-beetles, increase in complexity and relative size with absolute size of body. And this applies in evolution as well as development. Selection for increased bulk in the extinct mammals called Titanotheres automatically increased their horns from insignificant swellings to large forked structures over a period of millions of years. Here development has canalized evolution.

Then there are what Darwin called "correlated characters." The red colour of vertebrate blood seems to be in origin a mere by-product of the chemical structure of haemoglobin, without selective value. But in our lips it has been turned to biological account to serve as a sexual attraction.

Natural selection, it is clear, is a very various agency. It includes a number of rather distinct selective processes. It varies enormously in intensity, in type, and in direction. It is always relative to the evolutionary situation in which the species finds itself. Its *intensity* is related to the extent of evolutionary opportunity that is open: an oceanic archipelago, where there are few competitors and enemies, provides an enlarged evolutionary opportunity to any species that manages to colonize it. Its *type* is related to the nature of the competitive struggle that is involved, so that sometimes it operates solely or mainly to the benefit of the species as a whole, sometimes solely and mainly to the benefit of one kind of individual as against another. The *character* of its results is related to the nature and predispositions of the species that is evolving. In a bird or a mammal the pressure of enemies may result in a great turn of speed for escape: in a tree or a jellyfish it obviously cannot. And the *direction* of its results is related to the external environment, both physical and biological. An animal species in the arctic tundra and its opposite number in an equatorial forest will be pushed by selection in quite different directions. Natural selection is always operating on a number of different characters at once, often in conflicting ways, so that the result at any moment is a compromise, or a balanced equilibrium. It may result either in change or in the absence of change. In actual fact, it is always operating to secure stability in some characters, while at the same time it is often producing change in others: in other words, there is a balance between the maintenance of previous improvement and the securing of new improvement; and the balance changes with the evolutionary situation.

But in stressing the diversity of all these processes, we must not lose sight of their underlying unity. They all have this in common—they are all automatic and all selective. Darwin had the insight to recognize this common general property of all the operative processes of evolution; and we today are right to retain his single concept of natural selection as central, however much we distinguish different modes of its operation.

Natural selection operates through imperfection. Mutation, we may say, is an imperfection in the basic property of living substance, of reproducing itself unaltered: but without it, there could have been no change, and so no improvement of any sort. The wastage of lives in each generation is an imperfection in the process of living: but without it there could have been no differential survival, and so no further biological improvement. Imperfection is the necessary basis for selection, and so for any possible perfection.

To sum up, natural selection converts randomness into direction, and blind chance into apparent purpose. It operates with the aid of time to produce improvements in the machinery of living, and in the process generates results of a more than astronomical improbability, which could have been achieved in no other way. But it has its limitations. It is opportunist, and it is relative: at any one time it can only produce results which are of immediate biological advantage to their possessors, in relation to the particular situation of the moment. So it can never plan ahead or work to a complete design. Furthermore, it often leads life into blind alleys, from which there is no evolutionary escape.

I shall close this chapter with one concrete example of what actually happens when natural selection continues to act on a particular kind of organism over a longish period of evolutionary time. For this I choose the evolution of the horse family during the past fifty-five million years, because it is better known than that of any other family of higher animals. Most people are aware that the first known horses, popularly called Eohippus (Fig. 4, p. 49), were little animals about the size of a large terrier, with four toes on each foot, and that in the course of time they grew gradually larger, speedier, and bigger-brained; transformed their nails into hooves; lost all their toes except the centre one, which grew much larger; and evolved tall cheek-teeth with elaborate grinding patterns. This trend has sometimes been represented as what is called an *orthogenesis*— a uniform process, proceeding in a single evolutionary straight line, and at a uniform rate, as if it were the result of some inner urge towards a predetermined goal.

The detailed work of the last half-century has shown that this is quite untrue. The facts have been recently assembled by Dr. G. G. Simpson in his book *Horses*. There is not merely one line of horse evolution, but a whole system of branches, many becoming extinct after a shorter or longer persistence. In particular, the stock divided in mid-career, one part continuing the original trend towards efficiency for browsing on soft foliage, the other branching off towards efficiency for grazing on grasses with their harder stems. The rate of evolutionary change, as measured by change in tooth-shape and pattern and in limb-proportions, is much higher in the grazers than in the browsers. This, as well as the actual splitting off of the grazing line as a whole, can be correlated with a change in the environment during the Miocene period—the onset of a drier general climate, which led to the formation of great open grass plains where forest could no longer grow. And this in turn provided a new evolutionary opportunity for grazing horses. The actual process of transformation, both in browsers and grazers, occurs in a series of finite steps, each taking a certain period of time, and the earlier ones serving as basis for the later. The general improvement in the grindstone pattern and the general form of the cheek-teeth for browsing went on for more than twenty-five million years, but then became stabilized in all subsequent browsing species. Even this process had two distinct aspects. One was the so-called molarization of the pre-molars—the gradual conversion of the front grinders, which have milk-teeth predecessors, so as to resemble the true molars, which develop later and have

FIG. 5.—Diagram of trends in horse evolution (details in text, p. 55 ff.). Estimated time is indicated in million-year units. The geological periods are also given: P+R=Pleistocene (Ice Age) and Recent.

The rate of change, represented by the slope of the curves, does not pretend to quantitative accuracy. It was subject to considerable variation in related species and genera, so that the curves merely give a rough average (especially that for body-size). The sharp separation of grazers from browsers about 25 million years ago is well brought out, as well as the way in which evolution takes place in a series of steps, beginning and ending at different times.

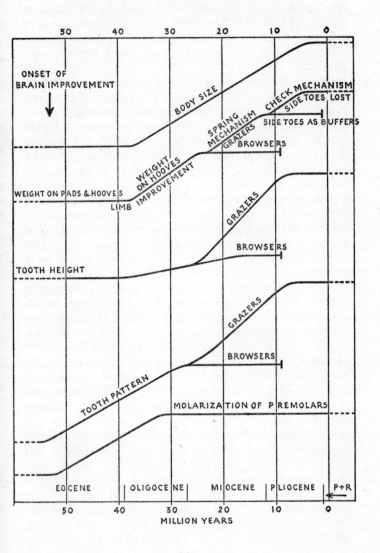

no "milk" fore-runners. This provides a uniform battery of grinders. The other was the improvement in grinding pattern, which continued for some further millions of years after molarization had been accomplished.

Then, at the beginning of the grazers' evolution, both tooth-height and complexity of tooth-pattern increased rapidly during fifteen million years or so, after which their teeth too became stabilized. Increase of tooth-height was necessary to prevent the teeth being worn down to useless stumps by the hard food, as well as by the longer life of larger animals. It began in the browsers, but in them never got very far. In the grazers, a new mechanism was developed. The teeth continued to grow out of their sockets, the roots themselves moving up and pushing out the buried part of the crown as its surface gets worn away. By this means teeth three and even four times as high as their fore-and-aft length were evolved.

The improvement of the limbs involved three consecutive steps. In the browsers, living in moister conditions, stabilization was reached at about the same time as that of tooth-pattern, nearly twenty-five million years ago. The stabilized browser foot was three-toed, all three toes with hooves, but with the main stress on the enlarged middle toe, the two small side-toes merely helping to spread the weight. In the early grazers, the first further step was the evolution of a remarkable spring mechanism involving the tendons of the still further enlarged middle toe, which gave the animals a greater turn of speed on their hard open plains. But this involved the risk of sprains and dislocations; and the side-toes were retained, though a little further reduced, as checks or buffers against this risk. Finally, in the line which led to the living forms, a second tendon was developed to act as an anti-sprain check mechanism: with this, the need for side-toes was over,

58

and they became further reduced, to survive as the vestigial splint-bones of the modern species. Degeneration of useless structures proceeds at a slower rate than the evolution of useful ones, so while the check mechanism was perfected five or six million years ago, and remained stable after that, the slow reduction of the side-toes continued for a few million years more. Some of the three-toed grazers survived for some time side by side with the one-toed forms before finally becoming extinct during the Ice Age. Various browsing horses survived virtually unchanged until the last of them underwent extinction early in the Pliocene. As machines for a browsing way of life, they had reached the limit of their possibilities even before the grazing horses branched off; and their stable phase lasted for nearly two-fifths of their evolutionary career. The grazers started their special transformation later: but even so they reached their stable phase at least two or three million years ago.

In addition to these obviously adaptive specializations, the horse family shows other evolutionary trends of a more general nature—notably towards increased size and towards greater brain-power. The latter was manifested not only by a greater relative size of the whole brain, but also by an increased size of the cerebral cortex, that part of the brain subserving intelligence and learning capacity. This trend began very early, and did not come to an end until quite late in horse evolution. But it slowed down markedly in the Oligocene and did eventually become stabilized. The horses concentrated on speed and the detection of distant danger, as against the detailed manipulation of objects close at hand; and so their brain capacities were tied in with their physical specializations and could not progress beyond a certain limit.

The trend towards increased size is of advantage in various ways; but it is self-limiting. Big animals auto-

matically become mechanically inefficient and un-
wieldy, and unwieldiness limits speed. With horses it
was the balance between the advantages of speed and
those of bulk which set the limit to their size. Some
extinct species of horses indeed sacrificed a certain
amount of speed, evolving into stockier and heavier
forms than the typical horses; while dwarf forms were
evolved in certain habitats. As a result, this trend is not
so uniform as most of the others I have mentioned, and
is better characterized by the maximum attained than
by the average. Browsers are generally larger than
grazers at any one time. This is presumably correlated
with the greater agility demanded of grazers on their
open plains. The co-existence of horse species of
different size and different build is a reminder that the
main trends of horse evolution were not single lines, but
branching stems, each separate branch being adapted
to some particular habitat as well as to a general way
of life.

This small-scale adaptive divergence superimposed
on a large-scale specialized trend is illustrated today
by the three main types of living species of equines—the
true horses of the temperate steppes, the wild asses of
the steppe-deserts, and the striped horses or zebras of
the African savannahs. Apart from the main fork which
gave rise to the grazers, the various branches did not
diverge greatly, but pursued a nearly parallel course.
In other words, the major trends of tooth and limb and
brain improvement went on independently in many
lines at once, though the rate of change of the various
characters differed in different lines. This parallel
evolution, this independent advance of many related
lines in the same general direction, is an extremely
significant phenomenon. The actual rate of change is
very slow. The increase in absolute length (height) of
horse-teeth, it can be calculated, varies from 1 per cent.
to 10 per cent. per million years of their evolution.

Their change of shape (a more significant character) seems never to exceed 2 per cent. for the same unit of time. The rate at which types classed as new genera succeed each other in sequence affords another measure. In horses, the rate is about one new genus every $7\frac{1}{2}$ million years. This seems to hold for other mammalian lines during the Cenozoic; but in other groups, such as the extinct molluscs called Ammonites during the Mesozoic, the rate was less than half as fast, as Simpson points out in his book *The Meaning of Evolution*.

The bones of fossil horses lie scattered in the rocks of four continents. They have come to life, in the hands of the paleontologists, to re-create their own evolutionary history and demonstrate to us their improvements. What will life as a whole reveal? Is improvement universal, and does it continue through the whole of evolutionary time? These are the questions that will chiefly concern us in later chapters.

CHAPTER III

Biological Improvement

"NATURAL selection plus time produces biological improvement." That was the second of my two evolutionary equations; and when I was summarizing the history of the horses, "improvement" was often the most obvious word to describe what was happening—improvement in their limb-structure, or their brain-power, or the grinding machinery of their teeth.

However, I must warn you that "improvement" is not yet a generally recognized technical term in biology. In fact, I should imagine that many of my biological colleagues would jib at its use. Some would shy away from it because it sounded teleological, while others would say that it implied a judgment of value, and that value-judgments were not scientific, or at least were outside the purview of science. However, living things *are* improved during evolution, and we need a term to denote that fact, and to crystallize our ideas about it. Darwin was not afraid to use the word for the results of natural selection in general, and I cannot think of anything more suitable. Indeed, as I said in the previous chapter, I believe that "improvement" can become one of the key concepts in evolutionary biology. The trouble is that the idea has not yet been scientifically explored or worked out in any detail—partly because it has not yet become quite scientifically respectable.

Our first problem obviously must be one of definition. Just what is biological improvement? Can it be scientifically defined? I think it can. In the most general terms, it is improvement of the various pieces of biological machinery by means of which living substance carries on the business of existence and survival. I use the phrase "biological machinery" in a broad and rather loose sense, as something analogous to man's machines, tools, and manufactures.

A piece of human machinery, say a steam-engine, has been improved in various ways since its first invention. In the first place, it has been improved by adapting the basic fact of steam power to an enormous number of different uses. Secondly, the steam-engine could be improved for any one of these special uses—we have only to think of the difference between Stephenson's *Rocket* and a modern express locomotive. Then the steam-engine, as such, can be improved in its general design and efficiency for any purpose. Thus, the fit of pistons in the cylinders of steam-engines has been enormously improved since the early days, when it was regarded as satisfactory if a knife-blade could be slipped between the working parts; and many other improvements in design, like what engineers call triple expansion cylinders, have contributed to the great improvement in the thermal efficiency in all steam-engines since they were first invented.

On the other hand, the steam-engine has its limitations. It is heavy, it cannot accelerate fast, and it cannot get up power quickly. It competes with other ways of generating power, so as soon as the internal combustion engine was invented the steam-engine could speedily be superseded in some fields. The new internal combustion type of machine, in its turn, made totally new types of use possible, notably for flying.

To return to biology, it is, I think, obvious that the changes I described in the previous chapter in the structure of grazing horses' limbs and teeth were really improvements in relation to the horses' particular way of life—rapid running on open plains, and eating hard-stemmed grasses. It is obvious, too, that their increase in brain-power was a general improvement which could be of advantage in many other ways of life also. Furthermore, the final differentiation of the horse stock into wild asses, horses, and zebras, was also an improvement, in the sense of adjusting the whole group to a greater variety of habitat.

The complexity of the biological process is illustrated by the fact that an almost identical way of life has been pursued by the antelopes. These, however, achieved rapid running in a different way, by utilizing the two elongated centre toes jointly instead of only the third digit. Further, they belong to a group which evolved the unique faculty of ruminating, or chewing the cud, familiar in cows. This enables the animals to bolt their food and then chew it at leisure and in greater safety; it may well be this special capacity which has given the antelopes their evolutionary success and made them a more abundant and diversified group than the horses.

There are plenty of other examples; but all the obvious ones are improvements in relation to a particular way of life, or in one particular function. Thus, as a flying machine, a modern bird like a falcon or a pigeon represents an enormous improvement over the clumsy Archaeopteryx of a hundred and fifty million years ago; and the Archaeopteryx over its ancestors, which could not fly at all. As regards awareness of the outer world, the eyes of a dragon-fly, which can see all round the animal in every direction, are an improvement over the mere microscopic eye-spots of early forms of life. Chemically speaking, the biological invention of haemoglobin, the red colouring matter in our blood, was a great improvement for all animals that require a high degree of efficiency in transporting oxygen to their tissues.

However, we need to go beyond particular examples: we need to visualize and define the *process* of improvement, as it actually happens in evolution. Time was one of the factors in our second evolutionary equation, and in considering improvement time is of the essence of the contract. If we take a snapshot view, improvement eludes us, and we see only competition and struggle. But as soon as we introduce time, we see trends of improvement. First of all, we see minor adjustments—moths becoming black in industrial areas, or the differentiation of a stock into separate species, as with the horses and asses and zebras. When we speed up our picture we see improvements for a particular way of life, as in the horse family as a whole. When we speed it up again to take in the whole range of evolutionary time, we see general advance—improvement in all the main properties of life, including its general organization. "Advance" is thus a useful term for long-term improvement in some general property of life, some general capacity of a type of plant or animal.

On the other hand, improvement is not universal. Lower forms manage to survive alongside higher; or, at least, simpler and less improved forms do co-exist with more complex and improved ones; and this means that *general* advance is best measured by the highest level of efficiency attained, rather than by the average. Furthermore, improvement is often restricted, and advance often limited. Over and over again we see trends becoming stabilized at a certain level of improvement. Thus all of the improvements that added up to produce the modern horses eventually became stabilized; and even large and dominant groups like the insects or the bony fish have shown no general advance for thirty or forty million years.

But, if we need depth in time, we also need a wide field of view. We must look not merely at changes within the single line, but at those taking place in the whole group—that is to say, in all the different species in all the different lines descended from a single original species. The improvement of the horses was only one among many improvements for different ways of life that were all going on at the same time within the group of the higher mammals—what biologists call the adaptive radiation of the group. When we look at improvement as an evolutionary process we find that it actually takes place by means of a series of such radiations of different size and scope. However, radiation is not a very convenient general term; so, following a suggestion of my friend Professor Westoll, I propose to use the word "deployment." Deployment, then, denotes the way in which the improvement of groups actually happens. An original single small group of similar inter-breeding individuals increases so as to become much more numerous, and much more diversified. In so doing it extends over more and more of the environment; it converts more and more different kinds of materials into its own living substance; and it does so more efficiently. However, deployment is always relative to the evolutionary opportunity open to it; and this always has its limits. Both the evolutionary opportunity and the limits set to it are partly determined—or at least conditioned—by the environment, partly by the properties of the living substance performing the deployment.

Darwin glimpsed the kernel of all this too. In his auto-biography he describes how the general idea flashed into his mind.

"At that time I overlooked one problem of great importance. This problem is the tendency in organic beings descended from the same stock to diverge in character as they become modified. That they have diverged greatly is obvious from the manner in which species of all kinds can be classed under genera, genera under families, families under sub-orders, and so forth; and I can remember the very spot in the road, whilst in my carriage, when to my joy the solution

66

occurred to me. The solution, as I believe, is that the modified offspring of all dominant and increasing forms tend to become adapted to many and highly diversified places in the economy of nature."

In *The Origin of Species* he amplifies this point:

"The advantage of diversification of structure in the inhabitants of the same region is, in fact, the same as that of the physiological division of labour in the organs of the same individual body. . . . A set of animals, with their organization but little diversified, could hardly compete with a set more perfectly diversified in structure."

You will soon see how true this last statement is. However, Darwin never generalized the principle—indeed he could not have done so since the necessary facts from comparative anatomy, paleontology, and embryology had not yet been discovered.

Let me again emphasize that the process of deployment is related to the evolutionary opportunities available and is conditioned by them. A striking example of this is provided by the groundfinches of the Galapagos Islands, the *Geospizidae*, which more than anything else persuaded Darwin of the fact of evolution. They are a small group of song-birds, undoubtedly derived from some species of New World finch which got blown out from the mainland and succeeded in establishing itself on this remote oceanic archipelago. The group now consists of four distinct genera and fourteen separate species, adapted for many distinct modes of life. Some are seed-eaters, others omnivorous ground-feeders, others insectivorous, others leaf- and bud-eaters, while one has gone in for a woodpecker type of life. All have evolved beaks adapted to dealing with their particular type of food, with the exception of the woodpecker type, which has developed the unique instinct of using a twig instead of its beak to pry for insects in crevices.

David Lack has summarized our knowledge of this group in his book *Darwin's Finches*.

This is obviously an adaptive radiation, even though it is on the miniature scale of a zoological Family instead of the larger scale of a Class or Sub-class or Order. An original single stock has deployed into an assemblage of separate and different species, and this has enabled the resultant group to exploit its new environment much more extensively. But this was only possible because of the evolutionary opportunity which that new environment provided. Since the Galapagos are remote oceanic islands, they have a very poor fauna, so that the ancestral groundfinch found a large vacant area almost free of competitors, in the shape of other small passerine birds, and also of enemies like hawks. In this region of low biological pressure, as we may call it, the strain could and did expand and differentiate, while on the mainland there were no such vacant niches or low-pressure areas available.

An even more striking example is that of the Hawaiian archipelago, where the bird family known as sicklebills, found nowhere else, has radiated into no less than eighteen distinct genera.

This relation of group deployment to competition is diagrammatically illustrated by the marsupials or pouched mammals in Australia. The Australian region was cut off by sea from the rest of the land world about sixty million years ago, after it had been colonized by marsupials, but before the origin or at least the spread of placentals, the more efficient group of mammals in which the young develop to an advanced stage within their mother's body. The placental type is more efficient than the marsupials in other ways too—in brain-capacity, in its greater accuracy of temperature-regulation, and in various details of its bony structure; and accordingly, wherever the two types came into competition, the placentals replaced the marsupials, either wholly (as in Eurasia), or very largely (as in the New World). But in Australia the marsupials had a free field, and there they radiated out into a number of branches, like kangaroos and phalangers, bandicoots and koala bears, which are found nowhere else, either living or fossil. The interesting fact is that this deployment produced results broadly similar to those produced by the deployment of the placentals elsewhere. Sometimes the correspondence is startling: among the Australian marsupials we find carnivores looking just like dogs; surprisingly mouse-like creatures; ant-eaters; flying opossums looking very like flying squirrels; marsupial moles almost indistinguishable from our familiar placental ones. In other cases, the same general niche is filled, but in a different way: thus both deployments gave rise to large and speedy herbivores, living on open plains; in the marsupial deployment these took the form of the kangaroos, but these get about by jumping, instead of by running, as in the corresponding placental types like horses or antelopes.

However, though the absence of competition permitted this extraordinary outburst of evolution, it also permitted an essentially less efficient group to survive. The result is that when placentals are introduced into Australia, they are met with very inefficient biological competition. Often, like the rabbit and the dingo, they spread and multiply explosively, to the detriment of man as well as of their marsupial competitors.

In general terms, deployment always leads to diversification within the group. It also always involves biological discontinuity—the splitting up of one original interbreeding group or species into many, each of which has then to proceed alone on its evolutionary path. A great deal of attention has been given in recent years to the problem of how biological discontinuity arises—how an original single interbreeding group becomes separated into two which can no longer exchange genes.[1]

It would be easy to devote an entire chapter to this subject of species-formation alone. The one point I must bring out here is that divergence to the species-level cannot take place without some prior discontinuity which isolates two sections of the group from each other. This is usually a geographical or spatial discontinuity, as between the populations of different lakes or islands, but sometimes it may be a genetic one, as with chromosome-doubling in plants. Where a population is not isolated, selection in relation to a particular habitat or way of life is always largely offset by immigration and the flow of genes from the population of other habitats. In any case, small-scale specialization involves divergence; and so the number of the separate streams of life that we call species has tended to increase steadily throughout evolutionary time.

As regards the actual differences between related species, I can only say that these can be of any kind and many degrees. So-called "good" species which never interbreed may be almost indistinguishable to look at, like the two tree-creepers of Europe, or various species of the fruit-fly *Drosophila*; they may differ solely in their ecological preferences, or mainly so, like the chiffchaff and the willow-warbler among our spring birds; closely related species may be differentiated primarily by size, as with our greater and lesser spotted woodpeckers; by preferences for different food-plants, as

[1] The paleontologist is confronted with forms which gradually and continuously change their characters in the course of time, until they become so different that they merit a new name. This can be seen in fossil horses, and in even more detail in the extinct molluscs, the Ammonites. The naming of such "successional species," as we may call them, is clearly an arbitrary convention, but necessary if we are to describe stages in a continuous process. Successional species are different from divergent species, which are real biological entities. Whenever we have a group with abundant fossil documentation, we find both successional transformation and divergence.

with many butterflies and other insects; or, as with many tapeworms and other parasites, by preferences for different animal hosts. In fact, species-formation includes on a miniature scale all the tendencies which are obvious in large-scale specialization.

It also involves much that is irrelevant to large-scale specialization. Many species differ in very trivial ways; it seems that some accident of geographical isolation has permitted enough genetic differences to accumulate for intercrossing to be no longer possible, or at least no longer to occur. The two kinds of European tree-creeper illustrate this. Their one marked difference is in their song: presumably they recognize each other by ear, and the primary barrier between them is this distinctiveness of recognition characters.

Much of speciation represents a frill of mere diversity, superposed on longer-range adaptive trends. Of course, each species is in some way adjusted to its local conditions from the outset, but it usually will not begin developing special adaptations until later.

As is to be expected, we can sometimes catch the process of divergent speciation on the borderline of incipient species or semi-species. Thus a number of northern hemisphere forms were separated by the Ice Age into isolated groups, which then remet when the ice retreated, after some degree of genetic divergence. The eastern and western woodpeckers known as flickers in North America, the black carrion crow and the black-and-grey hoodie crow of the Old World, are examples. Where they have met again, hybridization has taken place. The hybrid zone is broad in the flickers, narrow in the crows: the narrowness is presumably due to selection, the hybrids being less well adjusted than either of the two pure types.

How important slight differences may be is shown by the malaria-carrying mosquitoes of Europe. It used to be supposed that these were all of the single species,

Anopheles maculipennis. Today, however, it has been shown that at least six species must be distinguished, characterized by different preferences for fresh, brackish or salt water, by differences in the egg-floats, and by behaviour, some mating without swarm-formation, others requiring the stimulus of swarming. Most important for us humans is the fact that not all of them transmit malaria; and that of those which do, some can be more or less readily "deviated" from man to domestic animals, while others must be destroyed or their breeding-places eradicated.

In any event, small initial differences may be multiplied by the lapse of time. And so the scale we are using becomes important. Deployment can take place on any scale. It may occur even within a single species; this leads to the differentiation of partially dis-continuous groups or sub-species, each adapted to one part of the species' whole range: thus the pied wagtail and the white wagtail are the British and continental sub-species of the single species *Motacilla alba* of Linnaeus. It may operate on the scale of a Genus, as with the weevils of the genus *Proterhinus* on Hawaii, where over 150 species have been produced, or on that of a Family, as with the groundfinches on the Galapagos, or the horses throughout the world. It may operate on the scale of an Order. For instance, the order *Carnivora* among the mammals is the result of the deployment of one original tiny flesh-eating creature into lions, tigers, bears, seals, pandas, mongooses, and many other specialized types. It may operate on the scale of a Class—the mammals and the reptiles are the most striking examples. But finally (what is often overlooked) it operates on the scale of life as a whole.

The first major deployment of life was related to the fundamental function of building up new living sub-stance. As a result, living substance differentiated into three main kinds of chemical mechanisms: green plants, living on water, carbon dioxide and mineral salts with the aid of sunlight and chlorophyll; fungi, which require the simple organic substances resulting from the breakdown of other creatures; and animals, which need more complicated raw materials and so have to feed on plants or other animals. In addition we have the bacteria. These are often classed with the fungi, but merit separate mention, since some of them can play tricks of metabolism denied to other organisms. They include forms which can fix the nitrogen of the air, or obtain their energy by oxidizing inorganic carbon or sulphur. Many of them, however, have taken to parasitism, or live like ordinary (saprophytic) fungi. This primary deployment was clearly an improvement of life as a whole. It enabled living substance to utilize more of the resources of its environment and to do so more efficiently.

Each of these main branches differentiated in its turn. As an example, take the specialization of different kinds of animals for different methods of feeding. Sponges and clams are what we broadly call ciliary filter-feeders —they live on microscopic particles which they filter out from the water-currents that their cilia drive through their filtering mechanisms. Creatures like sea-anemones and jellyfish are tentacle-feeders. They can deal with larger particles, but only with those which happen to come in contact with their tentacles. Both ciliary filter-feeders and tentacle-feeders may either float free in the water or be attached to the bottom; but they never go actively after their food. As a variant we have the swimmers which strain out much smaller creatures from the water. The most notable among these are the whalebone whales and the basking sharks: they may migrate to regions where their food is to be found, but when feeding merely swim through the food-rich waters without taking separate bites at individual morsels. Then there are the active eaters, including the two large categories of the vegetable-feeders and the pursuers of animal prey; and of course there are special types like the earth-swallowers, earthworms for example; and all the parasites which live in the interiors of other animals. These are all results of the deployment of the animal kingdom for the business of getting food; if any of them had not been evolved, some of the available food-resources in the world would have gone to waste, so far as animal life was concerned.

All deployment entails specialization, and specialization always means improvement for a particular way of life. It is, therefore, always one-sided, and often involves the loss or degeneration of some characters—for instance, the side-toes in the horses. It may sometimes even involve degeneration in some original general property of the stock. As small-scale examples we may take the loss of colour-vision by animals that are active only at night, or that of eyes by the creatures that inhabit caves. But sometimes there is wholesale degeneration, as when free-living forms take to a fixed or sessile existence, or turn into internal parasites. Thus the sea-squirts or ascidians were once free-swimming creatures related to the ancestral vertebrates; but they settled down to a fixed existence as filter-feeders, and, in the process, lost all the characters which linked them with the vertebrates: indeed, their relationship would never have been suspected if it had not been for the fact that they pass through a short period of their existence as a little tadpole-like free-swimming larva—one of the startling discoveries of nineteenth-century zoology. In passing, it is worth noting that both internal parasitism and fixed and sessile existence get rarer in the higher groups of animals; and in the vertebrates they are not found at all.

Like military deployment, biological deployment is a movement in two directions at once, forwards and sideways. The separate lines diverge sideways so as to cover a greater total area of the environment. But they also advance forward. The separate lines become increasingly efficient in dealing with their particular sector of the environment, and often become improved in their general design as well. Bernhard Rensch, the German biologist, had this same general distinction in mind when he separated evolutionary processes into cladogenesis, or branching evolution, on the one hand, and anagenesis, or upward evolution, on the other.

Most single trends of improvement have a limit: they come to a stop, either by stabilization or by extinction. When stabilization occurs, it means that specialization has reached its limit, and natural selection cannot push it any further in that particular direction. Though it was an advantage to reduce the number of the horse's toes from five to one, it clearly would not be an advantage to reduce the one to none! And any further elaboration of the grinding surface of the teeth would make the grindstone too fine for what it has to grind. Advances in some aspect of general efficiency may also reach a limit. Sometimes this is due to limitations inherent in the mechanism which is being improved. For instance, a compound eye, like an insect's, is made up of a large number of separate visual units, each contributing a patch of light to the total mosaic pattern of the creature's vision. And this, by the nature of things, cannot provide such fine visual discernment as a camera eye like that of vertebrates. The dragon-fly's eye represents the limit beyond which the compound type of eye cannot be improved.

Sometimes the limit to further advance is set in a strange and unexpected way. The insects again provide the best example of this. They breathe by means of air-tubes, which convey the oxygen direct to the tissues. This sounds as if it were a more efficient method than our own, of using the bloodstream to transport the oxygen; and indeed it is more efficient so long as the creatures remain very small. But, as Professor Krogh showed years ago, it becomes more and more inefficient as size increases, so that an insect as big as a rat just could not exist at all, and all the most successful types of insect are far smaller than any mouse. Small total size in turn makes it impossible to evolve temperature-regulating machinery. It also limits the size of the brain and therefore the number of brain-cells in it, and this limits the insects' intelligence and learning capacity. The machinery for even an elaborate instinct can be constructed with the aid of a comparatively small number of brain-cells; but elaborate learning depends on the co-operation of an enormous number. Since high intelligence and learning capacity are of great biological advantage, we can be sure that insects would have evolved them if they could have. But, luckily for us, they could not. If it had not been for the insects' method of breathing, you and I would in all probability not be here today—the insects would have forestalled the vertebrates in the evolutionary race.

Now we come to what is perhaps the most interesting point of all: the succession of deployments made by a single stock during evolutionary time, from one firm base to the next. Every new deployment is, of course, made possible by the evolution of some new piece of biological machinery, which opens up new evolutionary opportunities. Let me first take a minor deployment—that of the snakes—a mere sub-order of the class *Reptilia*, but an extremely successful one. Their success is due to their having evolved a new method of locomotion, by lateral wriggling of the entire body, which is converted into forward movement by the scales on the belly, moved by a multiplicity of specially elongated ribs. Snakes are thus provided with what amounts to a continuous series of small limbs, in place of the two pairs of widely spaced large limbs of most land vertebrates; and this enables them to attain a considerably higher combination of size and speed in certain kinds of habitats, notably rough herbage and broken ground.

How did this new type of locomotion originate? We have as yet no fossils to give us a straight answer, but all the circumstantial evidence makes it reasonably certain that the ancestors of the group had to pass through a stage of existence underground as deaf, half-blind, and legless burrowing lizards. Many burrowing lizards are known; in all of them the legs get in the way and are reduced, and the animals rely more and more on the friction of the wriggling body. The one line which not only lost its legs entirely, but perfected the wriggling friction method of locomotion, was able to re-emerge above-ground. There it reacquired much of its powers of vision (but not of hearing) and achieved new evolutionary success as snakes. In spite of this great success in particular kinds of environment, the new method had its limitations. The need for scales precluded the evolution of hair; the high relative surface of the elongated body was hostile to the achievement of temperature-regulation, and the absence of limbs precluded the manipulation of objects and the increased intelligence and awareness that this could bring.

Later deployments often replace earlier ones. Sometimes the replacement is complete and total. Thus the only vertebrates known about three hundred and fifty million years ago were marine creatures without proper jaws, and with either no limbs or only one pair. They were totally replaced by the true fish, and all died out long before the close of the Paleozoic epoch. Sometimes the replacement is nearly complete: the group of proto-mammals of the middle Mesozoic epoch is today represented only by two species—the duckbill platypus and the spiny ant-eater of Australia. But usually it is partial. Many of the lines of the earlier deployment become extinct, and the entire group is reduced in numbers and in biological importance: the new deployment replaces the old as a dominant group. That is what happened to the reptiles at the close of the Mesozoic epoch, when the mammals began their major deployment.

This is the classical example, and I would like to describe it in a little more detail. The reptilian type rose to importance by exploiting two main pieces of mechanism for living in dry air—the large-yolked shelled egg, inside which the embryo is provided with its own food-store and its own private pond; and the dry scaly skin, which reduces loss of water from the body. It had some hundred and fifty million years of existence as the dominant group of land animals. During this period it underwent a major deployment, radiating out to give an enormous variety of forms—not only most existing kinds of reptiles, like crocodiles and lizards and tortoises, but all the fantastic creatures whose fossil remains we find in the Mesozoic rocks, including leathery-winged pterodactyls, the first vertebrate flying machines; fish-lizards like whales; fish-lizards unlike anything before or since, with huge paddles and enormously long necks; and the monstrous dinosaurs—dinosaurs armoured like tanks, dinosaurs speeding over the plains like ostriches, gigantic plant-eaters, and the most formidable beasts of prey that have ever existed.

In one line, however, the fossils show an unbroken transition from the reptilian to the mammalian plan of structure; and there was doubtless an equally unbroken transition in physiological characters. Indeed, one stage in the transition has come down to the present day in those living fossils, the duckbill platypus and the echidna or spiny ant-eater. They are mammalian in growing hair, in secreting milk, and in having a body-temperature above that of their surroundings: but unlike other mammals, they have no nipples and cannot regulate their temperature exactly; they are still completely reptilian in laying eggs; and they retain many reptilian features in their skeletons. They are, it seems, the sole survivors of a transitional group that we may call the proto-mammals, which had evolved enough new improvements to be able to embark on a small and limited deployment in the middle Mesozoic epoch. They occur only in the Australian region. Thus, while the low biological pressure of this region enabled the more advanced group of marsupials to embark on a deployment of their own, it merely permitted the proto-mammals to survive in these two lingering types. The difference between specialization and advance is well illustrated by them. Both are primitive in general construction, but highly specialized in detail, the platypus for an aquatic life, the echidna for feeding on ants.

But the major mammalian deployment was held up for over fifty million years. About half that time had to elapse before enough further improvements had been accumulated in the stock, and then it had to wait the rest of that long period until the stock found the opportunity to take advantage of its improvements. The opportunity was provided by the mountain-building revolution of the late Cretaceous period, with its violent changes in the terrestrial scene. In the course of ten million years or less, most of the reptilian deployment disappeared off the face of the earth. This was the mammals' opportunity, and their great deployment began, continuing in waves of improvement over another fifty million years. So we have what we may call the pre-mammals among the early reptiles, the proto-mammals which occupied a subordinate position during the main reptilian deployment, and the full mammals whose deployment eventually replaced the reptiles as a dominant group.

Within the main deployment, there was a succession

of minor ones each resulting from some new improvements. The earliest of these was that of the pouched mammals or marsupials: as I explained earlier, this was just in time to invade Australia before it was cut off from the rest of the world. The mammals demonstrate their biological superiority to the reptiles in the sheer facts of their deployment—they are higher because they have replaced the reptiles as dominant land vertebrates; because they have extended over more of the world's surface and into a greater range of ways of life; and because they have realized quite new possibilities for living substance, notably in self-regulation, in the care of their young, and in their capacity for profiting by experience.

Now we can see why lower and higher forms can survive side by side. There is an enormous range of evolutionary possibility open to life, and each plan of construction can take advantage only of a certain fraction of it. The higher forms are those which deployed later in time, to take advantage of possibilities that earlier forms had not succeeded in realizing. But they are no more equipped to lead the life of the lower types than the lower types are equipped to lead their life. Mammals cannot take the place of worms, or worms fill the niche occupied by protozoa.

We are beginning, I think, to reach the point where we can distinguish between the different kinds of bio-

Fig. 6.—Part of the machinery of higher mental activity (p. 91). Some cells, highly magnified, from the cerebral cortex of a cat. The cell-bodies are seen as black masses from whose bases a fine fibre, the axon, travels downwards; this conveys impulses away from the cell. The other processes (dendrites) formed by the cells convey impulses towards the cell-body. All these processes are interlocked with those of other cells, forming a series of networks through which impulses circulate.

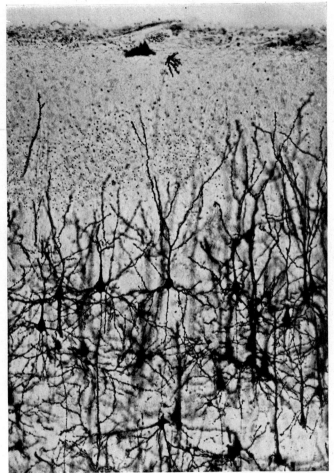

Fig. 6

logical improvement. Most improvement is specialization—it is improvement merely in relation to some restricted way of life or habitat. Some improvements, however, merit the name of advance. That is so whenever the efficiency of any major function of life is increased, whenever a higher and more integrated organization is achieved, whenever any radically new piece of biological machinery is evolved. Most specializations and most advances eventually come to a stop: but occasionally improvement continues. So we can conveniently define biological progress as improvement which permits or facilitates further improvement; or, if you prefer, as a series of advances which do not stand in the way of further advances.

Alternatively, we can consider the process in relation to three different standards. For specialization and detailed adaptation, the standard is the survival of a particular line of living substance. For advance, the standard is the general efficiency of biological machinery. For progress, the standard is the process of improvement itself. In any case, biological progress always operates in a step-by-step way, through a series of major deployments, each leading to the realization of new possibilities.

The realization of possibilities: that is perhaps the best way of viewing biological improvement. Living substance demonstrates its improvement during evolution by doing old things in new and better ways, by acquiring new properties, by organizing itself in new forms, by increasing its efficiency and enlarging its variety. For millions and millions of years living substance was confined within the prison walls of microscopic floating cells. Who would have ventured to prophesy what it could bring forth? The flowers carpeting the soil, the great trees with the singing birds in their branches, the glistening fish among the reefs of coral, the tribes of busy insects, the strength of the bull and the beauty of the butterfly, the elaborate fixed instincts of the bee, the intelligence and flexibility of behaviour of the dog: these are among the wonderful and admirable possibilities that have been realized.

There is of course a problem of values lurking in the background. How, for instance, can we reconcile the existence of so much cruelty and suffering with the concept of progress?

The female ichneumon-fly lays her eggs deep within the body of a caterpillar by means of her long sharp ovipositor—a beautiful adaptation. The young grubs on hatching out start to eat up the living tissues, rather as if a brood of rats were to eat their way through a living sheep. But the ichneumon grubs show a further adaptation. At first they spare the vital organs, subsisting only on the reserve stores of fat, the connective tissues, and the like. Only when the caterpillar has become full-grown and turned into a chrysalis do the ichneumons attack it radically, eating up all that is left inside the protective shell. Finally, burrowing their way out, they too pupate, turning into white cocoons on the outside of the empty shell of their victim.

In general, parasites have evolved at the expense of their hosts, often causing great suffering, as with the fly maggots that live in the noses of various animals.

Furthermore, the adaptations of parasites often involve large-scale degeneration in the parasites themselves, especially of locomotor and sensory organs. Sacculina is descended from a free-living crustacean: today it is little more than a bag of reproductive cells attached to a system of root-like processes draining nourishment from the body of its crab host. How can this be reconciled with the notion of advance?

There is no simple answer. The specializations of Sacculina or a liver-fluke for a parasitic existence are improvements from the angle of the parasites' own evolution. Pain and suffering are part of the wastage involved in the workings of the selective process. We must not expect to find human values at work in nature's day-to-day operations.

What is remarkable, it seems to me, is that the blind and automatic forces of mutation and selection, operating through competition and focussed immediately on mere survival, should have resulted in anything that merits the name of advance or progress. When looked at on the large scale, biological evolution *has* resulted—not universally, but regularly—in the overcoming of limitations, and has led to a steady rise in the upper level of life's achievements. It has produced co-operation as well as competition, and it has led finally to the emergence of values as operative factors in the process. These are facts to be accepted, not theories to be reconciled with other theories.

Advance and progress are possibilities of the evolutionary process, and have been realized to a remarkable extent during the history of life. This is the one major fact which links biological evolution with human values.

I must bring this chapter to a close by reminding you of the greatest improvement ever made in the machinery of life—the improvement of the nervous system. Before the nervous system could be improved, it had to be invented: the lowest animals are without one. Even the largest sponge has no nervous system whatever. Its first manifestation, which we find in creatures like polyps, is a nerve-net—an irregular network of nerve-cells and interlacing fibres extending all over the body. Its latest improvement is our own nervous system, with all its incoming and outgoing wires of nerves, and its central exchange and office and control room, in the form of an enormous brain filling up most of our head.

During evolution, the speed at which messages are

transmitted along nerve-fibres has increased over six hundred-fold, from below six inches a second in some nerve-nets to over a hundred yards a second in parts of our own nervous system. The brain's complexity of organization is almost infinitely greater than that of any other piece of biological machinery in ourselves or in any other animal. And the step in improvement from ape brain to human brain was the basis for the latest and most remarkable deployment of living substance. Finally, the improvement of the nervous system is linked with the emergence of mind, by means of which evolution has been gradually converted from a mechanical towards a conscious process. This extraordinary phenomenon I shall try to deal with in my next chapter.

CHAPTER IV

The Development of Mental Activity

ONE of the most famous passages in *Paradise Lost* begins with the lines:

"Hail, holy light, offspring of Heav'n first-born
Or of th'eternal coeternal beam."

Milton was right in apostrophizing light, one of the wonders of existence; but he was wrong in assuming that it had existed from all eternity. Light, in any proper sense of the word, did not come into existence before there were animals with eyes. The issue has been confused by the unfortunate habit of the physicists of appropriating common words from the vocabulary of human life, and using them for their own very different purposes. For a biologist, "light" should only mean a kind of awareness, a mental experience: for him, strictly speaking, it is a misuse of terms to employ it to denote radiations in the outer world. Photic radiations, if you like; but light, no. However, there are many situations where such purism is not called for; and where confusion is not possible, I shall often use "light" and "light-waves" in their usual equivocal sense.

Milton's very natural mistake about light immediately poses the tremendous philosophical problems of the relations between mind and matter. I want to treat this as a biologist—that is to say I shall look at it not as something static, but as a relationship which has developed over aeons of evolutionary time. For this purpose, colour is a better illustration than mere light. In the first place, colour, like all experience, is an experience of qualities. There is a qualitative difference between the sensation of red and the sensation of blue. That is a fact of experience : but you cannot explain the difference to a blind man who has never had the experience. Again, like all experience, it is a joint product of a complicated transaction—a transaction between photic radiations, sense-organs for picking up these radiations and translating them into nerve-impulses, nerves for transmitting these impulses, and finally a particular part of the brain for translating these into the particular kind of experiences we call colour. But all the elements in the transaction, except the last, are purely quantitative. The radiations which eventually give rise to different colour-sensations differ only in their intensity and their wave-lengths. The impulses which travel up to the brain along the nerves are of an electrical nature and differ only in their time-relations, such as their frequency, and in their intensity. But in the brain, these purely quantitative differences in electrical pattern are translated into wholly different qualities of sensation. The miracle of mind is that it can transmute quantity into quality. This property of mind is something given : it just is so. It cannot be explained : it can only be accepted. But we can study the way in which the mind-matter relation changes during the process of evolution.

Let me map out the course I shall pursue in this chapter. I shall begin by stating the problem in evolutionary terms. Life has two aspects, a material and a mental. Its mental aspect increases in importance during evolutionary time. Later animal deployments have reached a higher level of mental organization than earlier ones : the higher animals have a larger mental component in their make-up. This fact leads to an important conclusion—that mind is not a pale epi-phenomenon, not a mere "ghost in the machine," to use Professor Ryle's phrase, but an *operative* part of life's mechanism. For no evolutionary trend can be maintained except by natural selection, and natural selection can only work on what is biologically useful to its possessors.

Mental activity is intensified and mental organization improved during evolution: like bodily organization, it is improved in different ways in relation to different needs. This improvement of mental organization I shall illustrate from the field of awareness—what knowledge an animal has of the outer world, and how that knowledge is organized.

Most trends in mental organization were specializations for a particular way of life, and eventually came to a dead end. However, one particular trend was progressive, and led to the final emergence of mind as the most important property of its possessors. Tihs was the line in which experience became organized in the form of verbal concepts, and it resulted in the deployment of man as the latest dominant type in evolution.

That is the broad line of the evolutionary argument. It remains to define it more accurately and pursue it in more concrete detail. To begin with, the basic datum of our life is experience. During our existence we pass through a series of experiences—perceiving, feeling, knowing, willing. All of them are, in the broad sense in which I am using the word, mental activities. Let us be clear at the outset: there is really no such thing as "mind." Mind is not an entity in its own right, and our minds are not little separate creatures inhabiting our skulls. So it is much better to speak of "mental activities," though "mind" may often be useful as a shorthand term to denote mental activities in general.

Mental activity, as the past hundred years of research have clearly shown, is tied in with cerebral activity. It only goes on in conjunction with brains, and only with brains that are working properly. Secondly, mental activity becomes more intense, more varied, and better organized in each human individual during his or her development. Think of the mind of a man as against that of a child, the mind of a child as against that of a new-born infant. And in the microscopic ovum from which the infant originally grew, we can detect no trace of mental activity whatever. It also becomes more intense, more varied and better organized in living substance during evolutionary time. Think of the mental capacity of a human being as against that of a dog, the mental capacity of a dog as against that of a fish; in a worm, mental activities are barely detectable, and among the bacteria there is no trace of them at all, any more than in a chemical reaction. Further, as we have seen, mental capacities are always concerned with qualities, never merely with quantities. The sensation of seeing is a different kind of thing from the sensation of hearing; and all sensations are qualitatively different from emotion or understanding. Pain is not merely less pleasure or negative pleasure: it is a different sort of experience altogether.

For a biologist, much the easiest way is to think of mind and matter as two aspects of a single, underlying reality—shall we call it world substance, the stuff out of which the world is made. At any rate, this fits more of the facts and leads to fewer contradictions than any other view. In this view, mental activities are among the inevitable properties of world substance when this is organized in the form of the particular kind of biological machinery we find in a brain. The electrical properties of living substance provide us with a useful analogy. We now know that all activities in the body are accompanied by electrical changes—but changes so minute that they were only detected when special instruments were invented during the nineteenth century. All living substance, indeed all substance, inorganic as well as organic, has electrical properties, and all its properties have an electrical aspect. But these minute electrical changes can be intensified and utilized for biological ends. In nervous tissue they are utilized to transmit messages within the body: and a few fish, like the torpedo and the electric eel, possess organs for intensifying them to such a degree that they can be used to give dangerous electric shocks. I find myself driven to assume that the analogy with mind holds good—in other words that all living substance has mental, or we had better say mind-like, properties; but that these are, for the most part, far below the level of detection. They could only be utilized for biological ends when organs were evolved capable of intensifying them. These organs are certain specially developed parts of brains. It is by means of them that mind emerges as an operative factor in evolution.

The evolutionary approach brings out another important point about mind. Granted that natural selection is the only effective agency for producing change in biological evolution, a high degree of mental activity and mental organization could only have come into being if it was of biological advantage to its possessors. This at one stroke overthrows all theories of materialism, for they deny the effective reality of mind, or reduce it to a mere fly on the material wheel. Thus, for the modern biologist, the dialectical materialism that provides the philosophical basis for Marxist communism is an erroneous survival from days before the principles of evolution were properly understood.

This does not mean that we should neglect the material aspect. We shall get nowhere without intensive study of physiology and material structure and observable behaviour: but unless we combine this with introspection, interpretation and deduction from subjective experience, we shall not get very far, as the fate of the Behavourist movement shows. The metaphysician may persist in asking whether colour is something which inheres in external nature, or merely exists in the mind. The evolutionary biologist is not interested in colour in this way. He is concerned with the fact that new kinds of experience, like light and colour, come into existence during evolution, and that they can affect its subsequent course.

Colour and pattern have rather different functions in the animal's awareness. The pattern that an animal sees is in some sort a representation of the actual form of an external object. But colour is utilized mainly to detect differences within patterns. This it does by turning quantitative differences in the object (and in the patterns of nerve-impulses) into qualitative differences in awareness. A pattern of red and green that ought to mean something important to a railway signalman may, if the signalman is afflicted with a certain kind of colour-blindness, be perceived as a mere grey uniformity. However, once colour arrived upon the evolutionary stage, it became biologically significant. Colour-vision in one organism generates colour in others. Flowers develop distinctive colours to attract bees; wasps develop their black and yellow stripes to warn enemies of their stings; the partridge develops camouflage to escape detection by the hawk; the peacock develops brilliant plumage to stimulate his mate.

The mammals provide a suggestive example of this evolutionary relation. All mammals except the primates—monkeys, apes and men—appear to be colour-blind. They must have lost their capacity for colour-vision, probably because their Mesozoic ancestors had taken to a nocturnal way of life. Whatever the reason, in no sub-primate mammal do you find any blues, greens, or pure reds—only the range from black to white, and brown, yellowish or russet. But when the primates reacquired colour-vision, blues, greens, pinks and reds reappear, even though sparsely: the cheeks of the male mandril and the bright posteriors of various monkeys are examples.

New levels of mental organization thus involve new kinds of experiences; but they also issue in new kinds of observable behaviour. Behaviour is always the result of a flow of something—what many psychologists and most laymen call nervous energy. Unfortunately, the physiologists are driven to say "excitation," because *energy* is another word the physicists have taken over from ordinary speech and given a restricted scientific meaning. We may need a new term. Perhaps the word "neurergy" would serve: but this is a matter for the specialists to decide.

Knowledge of the material processes going on in the brain may also help in understanding the evolution of mind. There is increasing agreement that one very special kind of nervous organization is of great importance—the organization in the cerebral cortex of large groups of nerve-cells and their connecting outgrowths into self-reinforcing circuits of excitation (Fig. 6, p. 80). Circuits of this sort are arrangements for maintaining an organized flow of excitation through the cortex, on its way to become translated into organized behaviour. If they are interfered with, it seems that various disturbances arise, like pain and fear; while pleasure and what we may call integrative emotions, like love, are linked up with the maintenance or increase of their organized flow. Pain is thus in its origin a by-product of nervous structure: but, as I shall later point out, it can subsequently be utilized as part of the machinery of learning.

But I must pass on from the physiology of behaviour to the emergence of mental structure. The fact of mind's emergence may be simply demonstrated from the actual behaviour of a few animals. Consider first *Paramecium*, the microscopic slipper animalcule—that compulsory study for every elementary student in biology. Its normal existence merely consists in swimming onward in a spiral path. It does not actively pursue its food, but simply sweeps bacteria into its gullet as it swims. Now and again, however, it checks its advance, backs, turns a little, and then continues in a new direction. This so-called *avoiding reaction* is executed whenever the animal meets with unfavourable conditions, such as water which is not of the right degree of acidity for bacteria to grow in, and it repeats it until it finds itself in favourable conditions. This behaviour is mere trial and error, and neither learning nor purposive direction is involved. *Paramecium* must be in some way aware of the difference between more acid and less acid water, but this is almost the only sort of awareness we have any right to ascribe to it.

Euglena is another single-celled organism which swims in a spiral advance, but it has a little rudiment of an eye, a spot of pigment over a patch of specially light-sensitive substance. And so it is capable of what is broadly called a tropism; it directs its swimming in relation to the direction of the light that falls upon it. It has a primitive awareness of light, and it finds its way into the most favourable parts of its environment by utilizing this awareness, and not only by trial and error. The behaviour of an earthworm is much more complicated. An earthworm is capable of a number of reflex actions, each resulting from some different awareness—awareness of light, of chemical stimuli, of touch and pressure. And finally it has some capacity for learning. If confronted with two alternative pathways, it can learn to choose the one which leads to a more favourable result. That is a very limited kind of learning; but still it *is* learning. Finally, let me jump from worms to mammals. A rat can learn to run through a maze with a dozen turnings. And we all know how elaborate the behaviour of a dog can be. In dog-life, mind has certainly emerged as a major factor.

But the evolutionary biologist is concerned more with the description of processes than the demonstration of facts. He wants to understand something of the way in which the dual-aspect system of mind and behaviour evolves; of how mental organization is specialized and improved during evolution. However, this is an enormous subject, and all I can do is to illustrate it by way of examples from the organization of animals' awareness, in a broad and perhaps rather loose sense of the word. In the first place, the range of awareness may be increased. This is achieved by the improvement of different receptor organs. They are windows, so to speak, letting in different kinds of awareness of different parts of reality. Vision lets in movement and shape and distance; smell and taste let in chemical properties; touch lets in a knowledge of what is in immediate contact with the body; sound is used as an indicator of the distant presence of something significant—enemy, or prey, or mate. An electrical sense is exceedingly rare; it is confined to a few fish which find their way about by means of electrical signals that they send out. Pit-vipers have developed a unique type of sense-organ, in the shape of a directional receptor for heat-radiations; this enables them to locate the warm-blooded small mammals on which they feed. Sometimes new ranges of sensation are evolved. Thus bats find their way about by means of ultra-sonic vibrations, of a frequency far above that which can be detected by the human ear. These are emitted all the time while the bat is flying, and are reflected back from any solid object in the neighbourhood—a kind of glorified echo-sounding.

Bees do not use the same range of photic radiations as we do: they are blind to red, but can see a certain distance into the ultra-violet. Further, they are aware of something we can only detect by means of special apparatus—the plane of polarized light. This is because each of the units of their compound eyes is constructed in such a way that it can act roughly like a Nicol prism. This pre-requisite has been turned to account, and the bees steer themselves in relation to the sun's position even on overcast days, by taking advantage of this capacity.

Many phenomena of nature have never entered into the effective world of animals because there were no sense-organs to receive them. There are no animals with an awareness of X-rays or radio waves or magnetic fields: that had to wait for the construction of artificial sense-organs by scientific man. In any particular animal the performance of receptor organs—the kind of phenomena they admit—is a restricted one. It is partly restricted by the nature of living substance: thus the long electro-magnetic waves of radio simply pass through living substance and its secretions without affecting them, so that it would be impossible to construct a radio receptor organ out of such materials. Then awareness may be organized by relating the *quality* of a sensation to the needs of the animal. Thus, to put the matter rather crudely, sweet things taste nice because sugars are an abundant and valuable source of food. Lead acetate, which does not exist as such in the natural environment, also tastes sweet, but it is a poison. We can be pretty sure that if it had been as common as sugar, and sugar as rare as lead acetate, sweet things would have tasted nasty.

Then the *range* of a sensation may be restricted, so that only a few significant events come to the notice of the animal. Thus, the smelling organs in the elaborately branched antennae in certain kinds of male moths, while incredibly acute in detecting the smell of a female of the same species, seem to be unresponsive to every other kind of smell.

The sense which is most in need of restriction is that of vision: it would merely be confusing if an animal were to pay attention to all the visible changes going on in its environment. One of the ways in which this restriction is accomplished is by building into the brain special channels of flow which let through certain patterns much more readily than others.

Such patterns of sensory awareness are called *releasers*, because they conduct the flow of excitation through the brain, to release a specific pattern of behaviour; they are keys to unlock certain doors of action. They are found in relation to all the senses, but vision provides the best examples. Here I have space for only one or two. Let me first take the crouching reaction which young game-birds practise, even at their first sight of a hawk overhead. It seemed difficult to account for this without appealing to some sort of Lamarckian inheritance of racial experience—until it was shown that the reaction could be produced by a crude four-armed model with one very blunt and one rather long arm. When this is towed overhead with the blunt arm forward, it makes a rough representation of a hawk in flight, with its long tail and short neck: whereas when the model is towed with the long arm forward, the resemblance is rather to a flying duck than a hawk, and elicits no crouching reaction from the young game-birds. Sounds too have no effect. The releaser key, in this case, thus includes direction of movement as one of its necessary wards; but no detailed resemblance to a hawk is required.

An equally striking case is that of herring gulls. These birds have a yellow bill with a red patch near the tip of the lower mandible. It seemed difficult to assign any meaning to this in relation to courtship or threat. Eventually Tinbergen showed that it had to do with releasing the feeding reaction of the young. The parent regurgitates a small portion of food, which it then holds in the tip of its beak for the young to seize. Even new-hatched chicks which have never seen their parents will peck at a painted two-dimensional cardboard model of a head. By varying the model, it was shown that the red spot was the chief sign-stimulus involved, but that it must be near the protruding tip. In the absence of a red spot in the right position, the chicks would hardly beg at all, even from a model otherwise life-like. And Tinbergen produced a model bearing no resemblance to a gull's head which actually elicited a supernormal degree of response. Here the releaser involves a rather simple pattern of sign-stimuli.

Sometimes a releaser starts as a by-product. Thus, when the male stickleback's drive to fight is thwarted, or balanced by the drive to escape, the nervous excitation spills over and is discharged into another channel, that of digging a nest-hole. Such irrelevant spill-over activities are called displacement activities. In this case the incomplete digging reaction has later evolved into a sign of threat: the action has become stereotyped genetically in a new and more conspicuous form, with the red breast prominently displayed.

In a similar way, the head-shaking so common in diving birds has in the crested grebe been incorporated in ritualized form in its wonderful mutual courtship display, and the effect has been enhanced by the evolution of a striking ruff of chestnut and black round the face. In passing, I may note that here courtship display is not a mere matter of simple sign-stimuli and reactions, but an elaborate ritual performed by both sexes jointly, and enjoyed for its own sake, as well as serving as a bond between the members of the pair. Animal life can extend its range of expression as well as its awareness.

Releaser mechanisms are built into the animal by heredity; and they can only relate it to its environment in rather a crude way, and one which can easily become misleading. It is no accident that the only definite releaser known in man is the pattern made by a mother's smile to her infant. For more accurate adjustment, the animal must build up its patterns of awareness out of its own individual experience. I will give one example—our own perceptions. These are not, as is

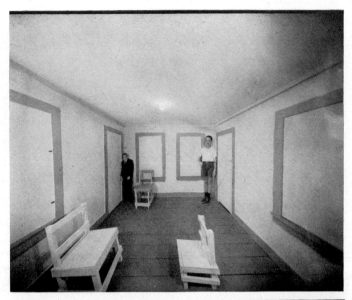

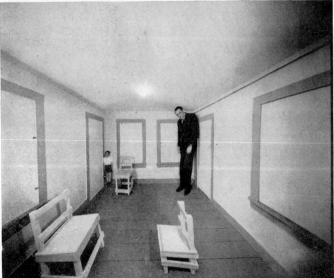

Fig. 7

often thought, snapshot pictures of reality projected into our minds, but quite elaborate mental constructions.

People who recover their sight after being blind from infancy have to learn, by a long and tedious process, to build distinguishable objects and forms out of the kaleidoscopic patchwork which is all that they at first discern. For a long time, they cannot even distinguish triangles from circles except by tracing their outlines with their fingers. A combination of data from the senses of sight and touch is needed for putting the three dimensions of space into any perceptions. A baby spends a large part of its existence in constructing, out of the crude sensory experiences of handling, touching, looking, the three-dimensional world of objects in which it will later live. The same thing holds with animals like chimpanzees, as is demonstrated by the fact that they can be taken in by the same illusions as we. However, their spatial world is not exactly like ours—for instance, they cannot learn to see whether a mechanical construction is stable or not. They will pile boxes on each other to get at a banana hung from the ceiling; but they never seem to acquire any insight as to whether the pile of boxes will stand. To get it to stand, they have to work by trial and error.

The same sort of building-up process goes on in the

Fig. 7.—An illusion showing how we construct our perceptions on the basis of our experience (p. 98). The room is distorted, but can be and is interpreted as rectangular when seen from the centre of the front wall. The figures in the corners are then perceived as if the back walls were rectangular and parallel with the front, whereas its right end is really much smaller and its right corner nearer. By this means the five-foot boy can be interpreted in perception as taller than his six-foot father, or conversely, when father and son change places, made to look like a midget as against a giant.

perceptual processes of all higher vertebrates, although the elaborateness of the construction varies a great deal. Thus, a horse is unable to bring its sensations of touch and vision together in the same way as a monkey or a man; and so the objects which it constructs in its perceptual world are not nearly so well defined. This seems to be the reason why horses shy at a heap of stones by the roadside. They do not perceive it as a heap of stones as we do, but merely as something unfamiliar. In passing, it is worth noting that certain insects, like ants, must be able to construct perceptions of a quite different nature from anything of which we have experience. They feel and smell objects at one and the same time with the aid of one and the same organ—their antennae. Objects for them must be smells with shapes.

Our perceptions are thus based on a mass of assumptions derived from what we have learnt by experience. This is why it is easy to construct illusions. They introduce false assumptions, which then make us alter our total perception.

The way in which we construct our perceptions, instead of merely receiving them passively, is well illustrated by the distorted room which Professor Cantril has built at Princeton (Fig. 7, p. 97). This has its floor and roof tilted and its walls at various angles; but all the distortions are calculated so that when you look at it with one eye (or photograph it) through a hole in the front wall, the perspective can be interpreted as that of an ordinary rectangular room. And because you are familiar with rooms of this sort, you automatically do adopt this interpretation. However, this involves interpreting the back wall as straight and square whereas really its right-hand end is closer to your eye, as well as being much smaller, than the left. A human being in one corner will therefore be interpreted as in relation to the illusory size you have given this end of the wall in perception, so that a small boy on the right will be perceived as larger than a tall man on the left (Fig. 7, p. 97).

There are, of course, many other kinds of learning mechanisms. One of the most obvious is based on a combination of pain with a conditioned reflex. Such a combination is a mechanism for avoiding harmful stimuli and ensuring the efficacy of useful ones. Professor Young's octopus learned very quickly not to try to eat crabs after an electric shock had been associated with one or two attempts. The two parts of the arrangement are brought together in a special piece of nervous machinery, for when a particular part of the brain is cut out, the octopus will attack a crab over and over again, even if it gets a painful electric shock each time. Here we see how pain can be transformed from a by-product of physiology into an effective agency of behaviour. On the other hand, sometimes the transformation is not readily possible, and then pain is not utilized in this way. Even severe damage will not cause pain in an organ which is not normally exposed to that kind of damage. Thus the tissue of the brain can be cut without any trace of pain.

Here I must mention one recent discovery, made by the German biologist, Professor Rensch—the fact that increased body-size may be correlated with increased learning capacity; of two closely similar animals, like a raven and a jackdaw, the bigger will learn better, though the learning process takes longer. The chain of causation here is roughly as follows. Increased final size of the cerebral cortex is brought about by its growing at a faster rate than the rest of the brain. So an *absolutely* larger brain will have a *relatively* as well as an absolutely larger number of cells in its cortex. A larger number of cortical cells makes more elaborate learning possible: but more elaborate learning takes a longer time. It is interesting to note that this holds not only for birds and mammals but for beetles as well. This fact is of great interest, for it may help to explain the biological value of mere bulk—why so many lines of so many different deployments of higher animals have tended to increase in size during their evolution.

It seems to be a general rule that the greater the complexity of what can be learnt, the longer is the time taken to learn it. The human infant can learn to recognize extremely complicated shapes, but takes several years to do so. A rat, it seems from the latest experiments, cannot, or does not normally, learn to recognize even such a simple shape as a triangle; or at least it does not discriminate it as a unitary whole from the rest of the visual field. Professor Hebb, in his interesting but difficult book, *The Organization of Behaviour*, discusses this and other aspects of this complicated subject. But what the rat does learn about the spatial relations of its environment, it learns very quickly.

An immense amount of work has been done on the learning reaction of animals. Some learning is a matter of simple conditioned reflexes. As Lloyd Morgan showed many years ago, domestic chicks will begin by pecking at all sorts of small conspicuous objects, but have to learn by experience whether they are good to eat or not. In one set of experiments, Lloyd Morgan steeped one kind of grain in a bitter solution. The chicks pecked at it, rejected it, and on later occasions refused similar grains without pecking at them, rubbing their bills as if they already had the nasty taste in their mouths. Then he repeated this with other kinds of grain, until he had to give up the experiment for fear the chicks would starve. In nature, this negative conditioning leads young insect-eating birds to refuse nauseous and dangerous creatures such as wasps, after one experience. The wasps' distinctive colour-pattern makes it easier for the bird to recognize them in good time on later occasions.

Recently I saw a young magpie in Dr. Thorpe's

laboratory which had been hand-fed by its mistress long after it had fledged. It had not learnt to look for its food, and it was only with the greatest difficulty that Thorpe was teaching it to feed itself when hungry.

Broadly speaking, memory and the capacity to learn complex situations and make complex discriminations increase as we move up the animal scale. As I mentioned, an earthworm can be trained, though with difficulty, to choose one of two alternative paths in a Y-shaped tube. A rat can achieve success in an elaborate maze. An ape can learn to react to what it sees in a film; and some gifted apes can solve problems, such as fitting two sticks together by a fishing-rod joint, by pure insight instead of clumsy trial and error.

But the capacity for learning may be adaptively restricted or specialized. Animals often learn some things more easily than others. Thus herring gulls learn to distinguish their own chicks individually after a few days; but they seem unable to discriminate their own eggs, even from quite differently marked eggs belonging to another species. Similarly, male robins will attack a headless dummy so long as it has the releaser provided by the red breast; but they learn to distinguish their mates individually.

Conversely, the possibilities of learning may never be turned to biological account. The most obvious example is that of talking birds like parrots or mynahs. They can learn quite elaborate phrases, and certainly sometimes show "association of ideas" by saying the right phrase at the right time. (One parrot cited by Lorenz, after not seeing a hoopoe for nine years, at once remembered and spoke the appropriate word.) But they never learn to associate words with purposes—for instance, to say "food" when hungry—in spite of intensive training. The potentialities and limitations of mind jostle each other in a strange and interesting way.

Sometimes animals in nature learn something both new and useful. A striking example is the way in which tits in Britain have learnt to open milk-bottles, first with cardboard and then with metal tops, in the last few decades. Careful enquiry has shown that the discovery was made independently in several areas, presumably by a few exceptional birds, and then spread slowly round each centre by imitation.

Some kinds of learning are quite different from anything in ourselves. Thus young geese which have been hatched in an incubator will attach themselves to birds of other species or even to human beings and follow them about as if they were their real parents. This so-called "imprinting" has to take place during a critical period soon after hatching, only takes a minute or so, and is then irreversible: once it has happened, young geese will not switch over, even to their own parents.

In evolution, the great divergence as regards the organization of behaviour is between insects and vertebrates. The insects rely much more on patterns built in by heredity, the vertebrates much more on patterns built up out of learning and individual experience, which means that their behaviour can become much more flexible. Higher insects emerge from the pupa stage with their instincts fully formed and ready to come into action; all that experience can do is to adjust the performance of their instinctive actions to the immediate situation. Vertebrates, on the other hand, largely build their own behaviour, and the more complicated its organization, the longer is the period of learning required. It is no accident that higher mammals pass through a longer period of dependence than any other animals, during which they learn the skills needed for adult life by experience and practice and play. Monkeys have a longer learning period than other mammals, apes a longer period than monkeys, and man the longest learning period of any organism.

In other words, during the vertebrates' evolution, mental organization acquires a time dimension. Mental structure in insects hardly grows or develops at all; in higher mammals it grows rapidly and transforms itself radically until the adult phase is reached; and even after that slow growth may continue. And in human beings, mental structure may continue to develop throughout life, even up to old age—we need only think of Verdi or Titian. This increased capacity for incorporating experience in mental structure is naturally correlated with a trend to longer life. Once more, it is no accident that insects rarely live more than a year. Even when they live longer it is usually the grub-stage which is prolonged: the adults' mental structure is still short-lived. This contrast comes to a head in the mayfly, which lives as larva for years, but as adult only for a day. It is equally no accident that higher mammals on the whole live longer than lower types, and that their life-span and their continuous mental development may extend over decades. This links up with another important subject—the role of communication and language in evolution.

The Austrian biologist, Von Frisch, has unearthed the secrets of the language of bees, and most extraordinary they are, enabling the animals to signify to their fellows the type, abundance, distance and direction of a source of nectar or pollen that they have discovered. This they do by variations in the elaborate dances they execute on returning to the hive. But bee language differs from human language or any communication system found in higher mammals in that it does not have to be learnt; and from any communication system found in higher vertebrates because it is for adults only. It does not have to be learnt because bees have no learning period: their language, like their instincts, has to be ready-made; it has to consist of genetically determined releasers, releasing genetically determined reactions. And it is for adults only because the young bees are mere limbless, eyeless grubs, with which no real communication is possible. Human language, on the other hand, has its roots in the need for communication between individual parent and individual offspring in higher mammals, where there is a long period of dependence. When the father as well as the mother is drawn into the business of caring for the young, the unit of communication becomes the family: and where, as in apes, the family becomes the extended family group, communication becomes a comprehensive social function, at one and the same time an instrument for education, a vehicle of love, and an organ of group solidarity. This, at any rate, seems to have been the method by which the distinctive human system of communication actually arose.

The curious fact about apes is that they can learn a great variety of tricks, but not how to speak. With great difficulty, chimpanzees have been trained to say a few simple words, and to associate them broadly with certain situations: but they can neither acquire a large vocabulary by imitation, like parrots, nor learn to attach precise meanings to words. They have a rich and elaborate system of vocal sounds, which they use to express and communicate their feelings; but they have no words for things, no way of describing objects or situations. Their incapacity for true speech seems to be due in part to an inadequacy of the motor mechanisms of vocalization, in part to an inadequate faculty of forming concepts.

I must just mention emotional states, which have two rather different functions in evolution. They may serve to reinforce drives to action; or they can indicate to other individuals of the same or other species what action to expect. Darwin wrote a fascinating book on this latter aspect—*The Expression of the Emotions in Man and Animals*. A cat expresses its state of anger and fright by arching its back, bristling its fur, spitting and snarling and baring its teeth. The snarling and the baring of teeth are what the biologist calls "intention movements"—a half-way house to a particular kind of action that is in preparation. But the arched back and bristling fur may be called enhancers: they make the cat look more formidable. The intention movements have been utilized to let an enemy know what to expect if he attacks; the enhancers are a bit of bluff which serves to make him think twice. Sometimes the bluff has evolved at the expense of the reality. Some male lizards, when confronted with a rival, compress themselves so as to look nearly twice their normal height, and add to the effect by erecting a bright-coloured crest along the back. But they do not seem to get angry, and they hardly ever actually fight.

One final example, from the work of Professor Lorenz in Austria on the social life of jackdaws. Jackdaws express submission to other jackdaws by bending down and exposing their most vulnerable part, the back of the head, to the beak of a rival. The effect is enhanced by the pale-grey patch on the vulnerable spot. The result is to inhibit the rival's aggressive instinct, and he then does not attack. The result is that a stable order of rank and social position is established in jackdaw society with the minimum of fighting. Jackdaws form more or less permanent unions, and the female takes the social rank of her mate. No male ever mates with a female who ranks above him in the social hierarchy. When a high-ranking male mates with a low-ranking female, the rest of the colony at once change their behaviour towards her, and the promoted "bride" may at once start taking advantage of her new status.

A dangling black object in the hands of a man, even of an old friend, will release a violent attack by jackdaws: it is a sign-stimulus for the situation that arises when a jackdaw has been seized by an enemy. The attack is accompanied by a loud rattling note, and this will rouse other birds to anger. Furthermore, experienced birds may give the rattling note at the mere sight of a potential enemy; and in this way the young birds learn what creatures to avoid, while if brought up in isolation they will not budge when a cat approaches. Here is a curious combination of innate mechanism and the handing down of experience.

The attainment of a high degree of complexity in behaviour often has unexpected by-products and consequences. Higher vertebrates are capable of doing all sorts of things which they never actually do in their normal lives. Here is one surprising example. Some birds at least have a number sense and can count up to six or more, though they seem never to exercise that faculty in nature. Professor Otto Koehler set jackdaws the problem of taking a definite number of peas out of a series of boxes. Usually they mastered this problem fairly easily, but sometimes they made mistakes: and one jackdaw realized his mistake. He ought to have taken six peas—two out of the first box, then none, one, two and one. He went back to his cage after taking only five. But then he suddenly came back and counted out his task by bowing his head the right number of times in front of each box. When he got to five, he went on to the next box and picked up and ate the pea he had forgotten. The main reason why men can count better than jackdaws is that they have invented symbols as tools to count with, in place of merely repeating physical gestures.

An even more relevant example is that of the higher apes. Chimpanzees are capable of behaving in many human ways if they are placed in human situations. They enjoy the learning of all kinds of tricks, like driving a miniature motor-car, or riding a one-wheeled cycle. Indeed, the more difficult the trick the more they seem to enjoy performing it. They enjoy tobacco and alcohol, though they never could do this in nature. They can develop irrational fears and phobias. They can become a prey to mental illness, not only to neurosis but also psychosis. In this and many other ways they foreshadow human possibilities—both good and bad. But these possibilities were never realized in nature, because their mental organization had not undergone the final step of improvement. Apes have constructed for themselves a spatial world very nearly like ours; they sometimes show real insight; they can even organize some of their experience into concepts. But they have not yet built a symbolic world. For that, there was needed the enlargement of the association areas of the cerebral cortex.

In man's mental organization the two crucial novelties are speech and the creation of a common pool of organized experience for a group. I shall return to them later. Let me first remind you of a few of its other unique properties. Man is the only organism habitually subjected to mental or emotional conflict. He is therefore the only one which has to practise what the Freudians call repression; but also the only one who is constantly making conscious choices. He is the only organism which has a conscience, a felt sense of right and wrong. On the other hand, a conscience is not something given ready-made, whether by heredity or divine implantation. Like every other part of our minds, it is a piece of mental machinery, constructed by the young child to meet the ambivalent situation that confronts it in its early years. The situation is the co-existence in one person—the mother or some efficient mother-substitute —of authority which is resented, and tender care which is sought and loved. If this situation is absent, as in infants brought up in impersonal institutions, conscience may fail to develop, just as chlorophyll fails to develop in plants raised in the dark, and the children grow up amoral.

On the other hand, because a man is the only organism with the power of abstraction and generalization, he alone can have a sense of right or wrong in the abstract, or an idea of ultimate ends, or any notion of values. And I am not forgetting that evil and guilt and sin are among the unique properties of our species, just as much as goodness or grace or virtue. We build our own mental organization from the ground up in a way that no animal does. The resulting constructions are exceedingly varied. In fact, there is really no such thing as the normal man, since there is no single norm, no blueprint for the mental buildings that men construct. Man has the possibility of integrating his constructions into harmonious wholes: though even then they will differ in their styles. But they are often no more than an ugly or unhandy collection of shacks. To abandon metaphor, man often fails to reconcile his intellectual and emotional conflicts in any sort of integrated unity. When there is too little integration, a man is so far from adjustment to reality as to deserve to be called mad. We must not forget that madness, like evil, is another unique general property of the human species.

This brings me to something more concrete. In man alone do we find experiences and activities purposefully pursued and developed for their own sakes. A kitten plays and obviously enjoys playing: but in cat-life there are no organized sports, like ski-ing or football, nor have cats deliberately devised games with arbitrary rules. Some animals seem to experience a feeling which deserves to be called *awe*; but only man has a sense of the sacred, to use Professor Otto's phrase, and only man organizes religions around that sense. Some animals certainly have a dim appreciation of beauty (some bower-birds even practise a form of art): but only man deliberately creates beauty and ardently pursues it. In the most general terms, by-products of animal life have become ends in the life of man. Then a very important point: man is the only organism to be able to think of things in their absence, or at any rate to do so effectively and habitually. He alone possesses the faculty of imagination, or can grasp, in a single act of experience, partly subconscious and partly conscious, a complex situation involving facts and ideas, emotions and judgments, the past and the present and the imagined future.

But I must return to man's two major uniquenesses: his languages and his common pools of experience. Man's language is unique in consisting of words—words for things and ideas instead of sounds or actions signifying a situation. Words, in fact, are symbols instead of signs. They are artificial constructions, tools for dealing more efficiently with the business of existence; so that language is properly speaking a branch of technology. Words are tools for thinking. Chimpanzees can construct some sort of concepts: but conceptual thought only became efficient and productive with the aid of proper tools, in the shape of verbal symbols. Like all tools, words need skill for their use. Human language is thus not merely a collection of words, but an elaborate technique. It is in fact the most complicated kind of skill in existence. The language of bees is a wonderful product of evolution; but in comparison with any human language it is as elementary as a mousetrap compared with a power station, or a primitive abacus as compared with an electronic calculating machine.

Words may be good or bad tools: some outgrow their usefulness, others have to be invented to fill new needs. But the detailed imperfections of words must not blind us to the unique value of words in general. Readers of Helen Keller's autobiography will remember the moving passage when the little creature, blind, deaf and dumb since the age of a year and a half, suddenly realized that, as she put it, "everything has a name." She had already been taught various associations, had learnt to use simple signs, to recognize individual people and places, and to respond to some of the finger-language of her teacher. But this day, when those fingers spelt out w-a-t-e-r on one of her hands, while her other hand was held under a spout of water in the well-house, she realized that this particular combination of finger-signs "*meant* the wonderful cool something" that she was feeling. As Professor Suzanne Langer writes in *Philosophy in a New Key*, it was no longer just a sign of wanting or of expecting water; it was a *name*, by which this substance could be mentioned, conceived, remembered, and thought about—a conceptual symbol. This was her first revelation of the meaning of things, it freed her from the prison of her frustrated and under-developed selfhood, and rapidly admitted her to a share in the possibilities of human existence.

Verbal language was perhaps the greatest technical invention of living substance. It enables human beings to communicate and share with each other, and in so doing, it automatically gives rise to the second major uniqueness of man—a common pool of experience for a group. This is not a pool in the sense of a static water tank. It is something which can grow and develop. The pooled experience is organized, and its organization changes and evolves with time.

Nothing of the sort exists in any other organism. It provides a new kind of environment for life to inhabit. It needs a name of its own: following Père Teilhard de Chardin, the French paleontologist and philosopher, I shall call it the *nöosphere*, the world of mind. As fish swim in the sea and birds fly through the air, so we think and feel our way through this collective mental world. Our life is a voyage of exploration through its vast and varied landscape; as with all other kinds of exploration, hard work and passion and discipline are needed for success. Each one of us can only explore a limited area in any detail, but we can arrive at an idea of the whole, just as we can have an idea of the earth as a globe without physically journeying over all its surface. Only by exploring it and utilizing its resources can a man achieve the dual task of building a self and transcending the self that he has built. It is a world of possibilities, not merely of actualities. Though jackdaws do not usually practise the elementary mathematical art of counting, their mental organization makes it possible for them to do so when the opportunity is provided. In the same sort of way, primitive man did not practise higher mathematics. He did not even dream of its possibility: but it was an inherent potentiality of his mental organization. The difference between man and bird is that abundance of time was needed for its realization, as well as opportunity.

The great complexity of human mental organization gives it an enormous range and depth of new consequential possibilities. And evolution in the human phase is essentially the adventurous and stormy story of the emergence of ever more of these possibilities into actuality.

CHAPTER V

The Path of Biological Progress

THIRTY years ago, Professor Bury wrote a very interesting book on *The Idea of Progress*. When I read it, I was surprised at the modernity of the notion. Its history dates back to little more than three hundred years ago, and it is eminently a nineteenth-century concept. Other periods thought in terms of deterioration from a Golden Age, or of cyclical recurrence, or of the mere persistence of human sin and misery, tempered by hopes of salvation in another life. The idea of progress could not have become part of general thought until men could see that, in one respect or another, they were improving their lot. In the eighteenth century, the chief emphasis seems to have been on the superiority of the civilized and cultured life of the period. In the nineteenth it was switched to the rapid improvement in man's technological control of nature; but there were many variants of the idea, ranging from the perfectibility of man through universal education to the Hegelian doctrines about the National State. Darwin's work added scientific respectability to the general concept; but in practice it was used to justify any philosophy of progress in vogue, including the Prussian conception of progress through struggle and war.

One of my earliest essays was on this subject of progress. As a young zoologist, I had become impressed with the overall trends to be discerned in evolution, and the need for studying and thinking about them as well as about the minor details of the process, or its underlying mechanisms. In particular, I realized the need of reaching a scientific definition of the term "progress" itself. On re-reading this youthful production, I find

Fox Photo

Fig. 8. A living fossil. The Australian lung-fish Neoceratodus has remained virtually unchanged for over 150 million years. In many features it recalls the ancestor of land vertebrates. (pp. 123 & 127)

that my ideas on the subject are still much the same. The only difference is that I then thought that biological progress could be wholly defined by its results; I now realize that any definition must also take into account the path that it has followed.

It is easy to confuse the two ideas of progress and improvement; so, at the risk of repeating myself tediously, I want to remind you of a few salient points. There are all kinds of biological improvement. There are adaptations which benefit certain individuals at the expense of the species; minor adjustments of the species; specializations of a type for a particular way of life; and advances in the general efficiency of biological machinery. But improvements are not something ready-made, they are trends in time. And most of them turn out to be finite; sooner or later, they come to a stop. Occasionally, one line of advance continues after related lines have come to a stop; and then you get what I called successional replacement, where a later deployment replaces an earlier one as a dominant type. The fact of replacement is itself a demonstration that there has been general improvement or advance. Putting the matter in another way, there is continuity of improvement between one group and its successor, as for instance between reptiles and mammals. We need a term for the sum of these continuities through the whole of evolutionary time, and I prefer to take over a familiar word like *progress* instead of coining a special piece of esoteric jargon.

In the light of these considerations, the human species, as the latest successional deployment, represents the furthest step yet taken in evolutionary progress. This is not just anthropomorphic wish-fulfilment, but a direct and necessary deduction from biological fact. Man may not be the measure of all things, but the difference between man and the simplest organisms is certainly the measure of biological progress. However, though biological progress has culminated in man, progress had been going on during the hundreds of millions of years before man came into existence. It was there, merely waiting to be detected.

It was with these distinctions in mind that in my third chapter I threw out a brief definition of biological progress, as "improvement which permits or facilitates further improvement, or, if you prefer, as a series of advances which do not stand in the way of further advances." Progress could also well be defined as the way which leads to ever-fresh realizations of new possibilities for living substance. But we have to consider its results as well. During the course of biological progress there is a trend towards increased efficiency in dealing with the challenge of the environment, and an increased independence of the changes going on in it. Both of these involve increased complexity of organization and efficiency of working. In particular there is a trend towards more harmonious integration of the individual organism as a whole. Progress, from this aspect, is characterized by an increase of variety-in-unity. Finally, and in a way most important, biological progress is marked by the intensification and improvement of mental capacity and its results, in particular knowledge and the organization of knowledge.[1]

[1] Simpson, in *The Meaning of Evolution*, gives a number of definitions and criteria of biological progress. Some of them, as he himself says, seem to be too general: thus the sheer increase in the total amount of living matter cannot be much of a criterion in considering the status of any particular group. On the other hand, to call specialization a form of progress would appear to me to confuse progress, which is rare, with improvement, which is common. He criticizes the idea of defining progress in relation to the possibility of further progress, on the grounds that this "cannot . . . be used to define progress going on or accomplished in the past." But this objection falls to the ground when we think of progress as a process and not merely as a series of static stages.

In general, it is refreshing to find that, while rightly rejecting any mystic "perfecting principle" inherent in life, this eminent paleontologist agrees that progress has occurred during evolution, though it is not universal; and that it is not unscientific anthropomorphism to regard man as standing high on any scale of evolutionary progress.

Another way of putting the matter is to say that progress is constantly leading life into regions of new evolutionary opportunity. Like other kinds of biological improvement, it goes in a series of well-marked steps. Its path follows a general direction, but sometimes makes surprising twists and turns. Each new deployment, after steadily advancing over its new terrain, comes to an impasse. There is sometimes a path out of the impasse, but it is generally a devious one; it is through its twists and turns that life finds its way into a new field of manœuvre; and this marks the beginning of another distinct step of progress. It is not too hard to chart the general direction of progress, but it is extremely difficult to prophesy the detailed course it will have to take to get from one step to the next. On the other hand, once we can look back on the facts we realize that it could have happened in no other way. Progress is inevitable as a general fact; but it is unpredictable in its particulars.

The nature of the process can only be understood in detail by describing how it actually happens, and studying the way in which it is related to all the rest of the evolutionary process. The best way to visualize these relations is to think of evolution as a tree, but a tree with a rather peculiar manner of growth. It grows on the whole upwards, but with a succession of branchings representing the different major deployments of life. Some of these branches run more or less straight upwards, some diagonally, and some more or less straight outwards; but in each of them the final twigs do not reach above a certain level, and fewer and fewer branches attain the upper levels.

Just as there is no such thing as absolute motion—merely motion relative to some other motion—so there is no such thing as progress in the abstract. It can only be defined, or indeed described, in relation to other kinds of evolutionary change, and we must take into account the restrictions and the dead ends of improvement as well as the onward continuity of its advance. Look at the history of living substance from this angle: what is the general direction of overall improvement; how did life reach this or that necessary new step or level of progress; and how on each new level did it come up against limitations or into dead ends? We want to know the pre-requisites, the accompaniments, and the consequences of progress.

I once tried to list the series of all the major steps in biological progress, but gave it up when I got to the fortieth. Here all I can do is to pick out a few illuminating instances. Before beginning on this I must make one point. The story of life's advance is not made up out of the imagination; even though the evidence is often indirect or circumstantial, it is none the less evidence. The biologist knows that evolution has happened. He looks at the results of it, as many of them as possible, and then reconstructs the picture of its course which will best fit the facts. When the facts are available in the shape of actual fossils, his picture will be more detailed and more accurate. But the facts of comparative anatomy and embryology and biochemistry and genetics are equally relevant, and any picture which fits them will not be a false picture; it will give a reasonable approximation to the truth.

One of the earliest necessary steps in progress was the reduction of the rate at which mutation occurs. I remember the surprise with which I first realized this fact. We know that mutation-rate can be controlled genetically: genes have been discovered which alter the rates of mutation of other genes, though we do not yet know just how this is effected. We also know that any molecule so immensely large and complicated as a gene would be expected to undergo changes in its chemical structure—in other words to mutate—at a rate too high for reasonable genetic stability, and certainly much higher than all normal mutation-rates actually found. Selection must have mutations to build with; but if the mutation-rate is too high, the building will keep falling apart. The necessary reduction of mutation-rate to a manageable level seems to have been one of the very first steps in progress. With the possible exception of some of the viruses (perhaps not fully fledged organisms at all), this step was taken by all forms of life.

The first forms of life can have been little more than naked genes; an early step in progress was from this simplicity to the cellular level of organization. A cell, for our purpose, is a microscopic but highly complicated unit of living substance, enclosing a nucleus with an accurately self-reproducing genetic outfit in it—in other words, chromosomes with an array of different genes along their length, and a mechanism for distributing them accurately each time the cell divides. This seems to have been combined, probably from the outset, with another vital step, the development of sex—in other words, a mechanism for recombining mutant genes from different lines. It used to be supposed, until very recently, that the whole enormous group of bacteria were so primitive that they possessed neither chromosomes nor sex. One of the most spectacular discoveries of the past few years is the fact that, in their chromosomes and their mechanisms of sexual recombination, they possess essentially the same genetic equipment as you or I or any other organism.

Next, I want to say a word about the step to the many-celled condition in animals. This was indispensable for the attainment of more than microscopic size and more than an elementary degree of division of labour among the tissues and organs of the body. But it was not universally taken. The protozoa are organized on the basis of a single cell-unit; but they are among the most successful of animals, swarming in the sea, in the soil, in fresh water, in the interiors of other animals. This fact well illustrates the difference between success and advance. There is room in the world for microscopic animals as well as large ones. The protozoa fill a large part of the microscopic niche very successfully, and in a way that would be impossible for animals of larger bulk. Theoretically, the step to the many-celled condition could have been taken in two rather different ways—either by way of a colony of separate cells, or by the cutting up of a single highly differentiated cell with several nuclei in it, into a number of cellular units. It looks as if the first was the method adopted by the sponges. In any case, the sponges have remained throughout their evolution as rather loosely knit aggregates of cells; and they have never evolved such elementary pre-requisites of further progress as a mouth or a nervous system. They represent a branch that came inevitably to a dead end.

Professor Hadzi of Yugoslavia has recently made the interesting suggestion that the rest of the many-celled animals, the so-called Metazoa, owe their origin to the second method. He suggests that they originated from some complicated protozoan belonging to the group of ciliates, of which the Paramecium I mentioned in my last chapter is an example. It would then have had to cut itself up into a number of cellular units, each with a nucleus, the process culminating in the emergence of an extremely small and simple kind of worm. We find such creatures today among the Flatworms. They consist of little more than a layer of cells on the outside, equipped with cilia or microscopic whip-lashes for movement, and a mouth leading in, not to a digestive cavity, but to a densely packed mass of cell-units which pick up the food mechanically like so many amoebae. This suggestion is far from being generally accepted, but it is useful to help one to picture the way in which this step of progress might actually have been achieved.

The next indispensable step involves three apparently

different but actually inter-connected developments. These are bilateral symmetry; the exploration of the environment for food by forward movement; and finally the formation of a head—the gradual concentration, in the front part of the body, of the mouth, the primitive brain, and the main sense-organs. We are apt to take these improvements for granted; but, though they were indispensable for progress, they were not present in the great majority of earlier forms of life, and one or other of them has often been abandoned during the further evolution of animals. This happened with all the creatures that took to a fixed existence, or went over from active searching for food to filter-feeding or tentacle-feeding, to random crawling or floating—sea-anemones and jellyfish, sea-lilies and clams, sea-urchins and barnacles. And it is quite clear that any animals that lost any one of this set of improvements were thereby put out of the path of further progress. Headless animals are often successful; but they are in a blind alley.

One way of escaping from blind alleys may be that which has been given the rather formidable name of *paedomorphosis*—prolonging an early developmental stage into adult life and going on from there. I have already mentioned the likelihood that insects may be thus derived from the newly hatched stage of myria-pods, with its three pairs of legs. Garstang has made the more drastic suggestion that the free-swimming larva of some bottom-living form related to the echinoderms may have, by paedomorphosis, provided the starting-point for the evolution of the great group of vertebrates. This is highly speculative, and may never be confirmed by other evidence: but it is worth bearing in mind as a possibility. Certainly the vertebrate plan of construction has more affinities in this quarter than with the plan of any adult invertebrate type.

Now I must make a big jump. In the next stage of

animal progress, over hundreds of millions of years, there must have been parallel advances in many different lines—advances in efficiency and in integrated complexity. Thus, the three main groups which have evolved out of the early many-celled Metazoa—the molluscs, the arthropods and the vertebrates—all developed highly organized digestive and circulatory systems, highly efficient tissues like muscles and nerves, and highly elaborate sense-organs, like pattern-forming eyes, while they were still aquatic. It comes as something of a shock to realize that this could not have been achieved without death, in the sense of the obligatory death of all the body except its germ-cells. The distinction between non-reproducing individual body or *soma* and immortal reproductive tissue or *germ-plasm*, first made by Weismann, is an important one, even though it is not always quite so clear-cut as he supposed. In Protozoa, death in this sense does not exist: the individual simply divides into two. In Metazoa the separation begins; and it grows sharper during their evolution. It grows sharper in two rather different ways. The continuing sexual germ-plasm becomes more rigidly separated at an early stage in development. And the somatic tissues lose their capacity for non-sexual reproduction. Many polyps and worms, for instance, can still reproduce by fission or make new individuals by budding. But even this seems to be impossible after a certain level of organization has been reached. At any rate it never occurs in animals with a highly organized body consisting of specialized tissues. For the Metazoa, death was thus a pre-requisite for further progress; it is the price life had to pay for individuality and the efficiency of its biological machinery: and we continue to pay that price.

Among the molluscs and the arthropods are to be found some very successful groups, like the snails or the crabs or the insects: the insects indeed are in one way the most successful of all types, in that they have given rise to more different species than any other. But of all these none was capable of indefinite progress. This was reserved for the vertebrates. The earliest vertebrates had many pre-requisites for further progress. They were active searchers for food; their method of swimming with the aid of a tail gave them greater speed and power than any of their competitors; and they were capable of growing to a larger size. Perhaps I should say that the scale of their construction is larger than that of any other kind of animal. The smallest vertebrate is hundreds or thousands of times larger than the smallest mollusc or arthropod, and no mollusc attains even one-tenth, no arthropod even one-hundredth, of the bulk of the biggest fish, still less of the biggest mammals.

Further, a point which is often forgotten, their organization is more flexible. Their skeleton is made of living and adjustable material, like bone and cartilage, instead of dead secretions; and their tendons can adapt themselves to the tensions to which they are subjected during growth. Thus their whole structural framework can grow and adjust itself continuously, instead of moulting from one pre-determined piece of body armour into another, as in arthropods. In addition, they are capable of attaining a much greater flexibility of behaviour. They have evolved an internal environment which is both more flexible and more independent of outer changes than that of any other group. The bloodstream of higher vertebrates regulates its chemical composition with extraordinary accuracy, and in this way, as well as by its self-regulatory mechanism of temperature-control, lays the foundation for a high degree of continuity and accuracy of mental activities. Meanwhile the development of the system of endocrine glands, secreting hormones into the blood, makes possible a new and more flexible integration.

Before the appearance of the early vertebrates we have reached the stage at which evolution is documented by well-preserved fossils—the stage comparable to that of recorded history in the affairs of man. Accordingly, we can now often detect the actual twists and turns of progress. Take the successful occupation of the land by animals—a step which only occurred well on in the last quarter of evolutionary time. On land, the animal is confronted with a greater range and rapidity of change in environmental conditions than in water. This means a need for greater acuteness and range of sense-organs, and puts a premium on learning rapidly by experience. On land, again, not only was there an obvious advantage in attaining a high constant body-temperature, but it was easier, for various physiological reasons, to attain it. The stimuli of land life thus provided various opportunities for progress; and only the vertebrates were capable of taking full advantage of those opportunities. Even the insects could not climb these further steps—they are too small to have a constant temperature or to be very intelligent, and too rigidly made for flexibility of structure or behaviour. In passing, their inflexibility and their small size are the reasons for the enormous number of their species—each species tends to have a smaller coverage, so to speak, of the environment.

However, for the vertebrates to achieve land life they had to pass through a narrow and devious channel, some three hundred million years ago, during the Devonian period. There were various pre-requisites for this step in progress. In the first place, there had to be a change of climate—a desiccation which led to a drying out of the fresh waters of the world. Then, the invaders of the land, the future ancestors of ourselves, had to be fresh-water fish: marine fish were out of the running. They had still to retain lobe-shaped fins, widely spaced out along the body, on which they rested while on the bottom of the water: so all fish which had specialized for streamlined speed in open waters were out of the running also. Finally, they had to have a swim-bladder which was open to the gullet, and was therefore capable of acting as an accessory organ of respiration by gulping in air.

In the Devonian period there was a whole group of fish of this type, adapted to bottom-living in stagnant fresh waters—the lung-fish, in the broad sense of the word (Fig. 8, p. 112). When they were caught in increasingly stagnant water by the change of climate, they could survive by getting from one pool to another in case of need. In those which adopted this method, the air-bladder became a little more of a lung; their fins became better able to support their weight when out of water. So the first step in the conquest of the land was, strictly speaking, not an adaptation to land life at all, but merely an adaptation for continuing aquatic life by getting from one pool of water to another as quickly as possible. However, once this step had been taken, a new evolutionary opportunity was open. By means of minor further improvements their fins could become walking legs, and their air-bladders could become nothing but lungs. With these improvements the animals were able to spend the whole of their adult life out of water, so long as they spent it in moist conditions.

Another striking twist in the path of progress occurred during the origin of the mammals. They had, it seems, to pass through a phase of their existence as small and insignificant nocturnal creatures, in the course of which they lost the capacity for colour-vision. Their very insignificance enabled them to survive during the long period when the land was dominated by powerful and specialized types of reptile. Their opportunity came when a great mountain-building revolution occurred, at the close of the Mesozoic epoch. The accompanying changes in climate, and in the distribution of land and sea, eventually resulted in the extinction of many of their reptilian competitors and put the rest at a disadvantage. The mammals were then able to profit by their new combination of capacities—temperature-regulation, and caring for their young; and so were able to emerge into the light of day, and to spread and multiply exceedingly, though they seem not to have reacquired colour-vision until the emergence of monkeys and apes.

Meanwhile, the birds had replaced the pterodactyls as conquerors of the air, and during the subsequent period they arrived at a delicacy of temperature-regulation equal to that of the mammals. They also became capable of speeds greater than that of any other organism—speeds which were only excelled by aeroplanes a bare twenty years ago. They were very successful, and they achieved a number of important advances, but they cut themselves off from progress by their specialization. Their fore-limbs are so thoroughly specialized as flying organs that they have become unusable for any other function; they are incapable of use as hands, and hands were a pre-requisite for further progress.

Long before the end of the Cenozoic epoch, most of the possibilities available to living substance had been exhausted, in one animal group or another. Speed I have just mentioned. Size had reached a point where it became self-defeating; the chemical composition of the blood had become fully constant; the efficiency of nervous conduction, of sense-organs, of digestive systems, and of mechanical construction, had all reached limits of one sort or another. Only one feature remained capable of improvement—brain organization and behaviour. Only a greater flexibility of behaviour, and a higher organization of awareness, enabled living substance to become capable of conceptual thought and symbolic language; and these, as we saw, are the two distinguishing marks of man, and the basis of the latest deployment of life.

Here again the new step could not be reached except through a tortuous channel. The precursor of man had to pass through the stage of being a monkey. It had to give up the usual practice of mammals, of producing many young at a birth. As J. B. S. Haldane has pointed out, the presence of many young in the uterus gives rise to an acute struggle for existence between them before birth; and in this competition, general rapidity of growth and development is at a premium. Only in creatures which normally produce one young at a birth was it possible for the general rate of development to be slowed down, so as to provide a long learning period. Monkeys live in trees, and they use their hands as well as feet for climbing. They also use their hands for manipulating their food, and have developed binocular vision for its better detection. This combination of handling and seeing was necessary for the better organization of experience. Tree life thus laid the foundation both for our clearer definition of objects by conceptual thought, and for our fuller control of them by tools and machines tens of millions of years later. However, two further turnings had to be taken before this could come about. First, monkeys had to become apes. Apes get around mainly by swinging with their arms, not by climbing with all four limbs. This made it possible for their hind-limbs to become differentiated as supporting feet. Finally, it was necessary for the apes to descend from the trees. This paved the way for the fully erect posture of our own species; and made possible the freeing of the hands for the sole job of manipulation. And this, in turn, was the pre-requisite for the last step in biological progress—the attainment of true speech and conceptual thinking.

Looking back into the past we see clearly enough that conceptual thought could only have arisen in an animal as against a plant; in a multicellular animal; in an actively feeding animal, with bilateral symmetry and a head; in one with a highly differentiated bodily organization, which was therefore doomed to die; in a vertebrate as against a mollusc or an arthropod; in a land vertebrate as against a fish; and among land vertebrates, only in a placental mammal with a constant temperature. And finally, it could have arisen only in a mammal which had become gregarious, which had a long period of learning and experience, which produced only one young at a birth, and which had recently become terrestrial after a long spell of life in the trees. Clearly, the path of progress is both devious and unique!

Now let us look at the process from another angle. My grandfather, Thomas Henry Huxley, was among the first to focus attention on what he called "persistent types"—animals or plants which remain unchanged over enormous periods of time while the life around them is changing and evolving. Already in 1862 he wrote: "In view of the immense diversity of known animal and vegetable forms, and the enormous length of time indicated by the accumulation of fossiliferous strata, the only circumstances to be wondered at is not that the changes of life have been so great, but that they have been so small." In 1870, he reviewed the whole subject. After pointing out that "so long ago as the Miocene epoch, every important group in every important Order of Mammalia was already represented," he concluded—"the significance of persistent types, and the small amount of change which has taken place even in those forms which can be shown to have been modified, becomes greater and greater in my eyes the longer I occupy myself with the biology of the past."

Persistence of type, we now realize, is the demonstration of the fact that natural selection can and does produce stability as well as change, and that the restriction of improvement is a commoner phenomenon than its continuance. Persistence of type can be best looked at in the light of the facts about the major deployments of life. Then we see that there are two kinds of persistence. There is the persistence of a few survivors from a once-abundant group—so-called "living fossils," like the duckbill platypus; and that of a whole successful group without reduction in numbers of species and without any important change in type—for instance, the ants. There is as yet no generally recognized term for this latter phenomenon—I shall simply speak of persistent groups.

Living fossils are the more spectacular. The classical and most extreme example is the little sea-shell called Lingula, which is almost indistinguishable from its ancestors found in rocks that were laid down four hundred million years ago. A more familiar one is that of the oysters. As Simpson says, an oyster from two hundred million years ago would look perfectly familiar to us if served in a restaurant today. The common opossum of the New World is a survivor from the end of the Mesozoic epoch—over sixty million years ago—but at that time opossums were one of the most advanced forms of animal life. I have already mentioned the Maidenhair tree, or Gingko, that grows so well in the streets of American towns, and was saved from extinction by being grown as a sacred tree in temple enclosures in China. It is the only survivor of an early type of tree, producing active spermatozoa which swim down the pollen-tubes—a reminder of the still remoter epoch when all land plants had to effect their fertilization by means of spermatozoa swimming freely in a film of water. The Australian lung-fish is one of three survivors from a once-abundant group. It is almost identical with the ancestral Ceratodus which inhabited the fresh waters of the Triassic over 150 million years back in time (Fig. 8, p. 112). Latimeria is a final example, which shows that startling discoveries can still be made in biology. Latimeria is the name of a rather primitive kind of fish, more nearly related to lung-fish than to modern Teleosts, one single specimen of which was recently brought up alive by a fishing vessel off the coast of South Africa. Many other examples of this general type of fish are known, but they are all fossils, and they all date back sixty million years or more. A reward has been offered for further specimens, but so far none has been forthcoming.

The persistence of groups may not be so spectacular, but it is really more interesting as an evolutionary phenomenon. Perhaps the most remarkable example is that of the ants, because they are among the highest and most successful of insects. Ants of many genera are often found in amber from the Baltic, which is the fossilized resin of long-dead conifers. Every detail of their structure may be preserved in the amber, and thus we find that they differ in no essentials from genera of ants living today. Baltic amber is actually found in rocks of the Oligocene period, laid down about thirty-five million years ago; but it now seems to be established that it has got there secondarily, and was originally produced by trees growing on land which no longer exists, at least fifty million years ago. So ants, as a group, have not changed in any essentials for this enormous length of time (Fig. 9, p. 129).

This is merely an illustration of the fact I brought out in an earlier chapter, that, as a group deploys, the kind and degree of improvement possible to it becomes progressively restricted with the passage of time. Quite early in the deployment of a Class, all its separate Orders have separated out; after that we find no new Order emerging; later, no new Families;[1] and finally more and more persistent Genera. Other successful groups besides

[1] This statement requires some qualification. New Families may arise when a brand-new evolutionary opportunity is provided, as with the groundfinches of the Galapagos archipelago.

Fig. 9

British Museum (Natural History)

Persistence of type in a successful group (p. 128). The ant
genus Camponotus is a flourishing one to-day: this specimen,
beautifully preserved in Baltic amber, proves that it has been
stabilized for at east 50 million years.

ants show the same phenomenon. Thus, birds have undergone no improvement as flying machines since the Miocene period, some twenty million years ago; and the so-called Teleosts, the most successful and abundant and familiar group of fish, have undergone no improvement as swimming machines since much earlier; though in both cases new species are still being produced.

The whole question of persistence links up with what I called the successional replacement of groups. Living fossils are the rare survivors of an old deployment that has suffered reduction; persistent groups are later deployments which are still successful, but which have become so specialized in all their branches that they are incapable of any major change of type. Very occasionally a specialized line may give rise to another, adapted to a different way of life. Perhaps the best example of this is the development of the whalebone whales (which are large-scale filter-feeders) from the toothed whales (which actively pursue large prey). Even this is only ringing the changes on the single whale type. In general the rise of a new group to success is correlated with a reduction of the group from which it has risen. The mammals are perhaps the most interesting example of this, for their fall is associated with our rise. Since the beginning of the human deployment they have suffered a marked reduction. The number of specialized lines which have become extinct is large—for instance, the ground-sloths and the sabre-toothed tigers; and others have become much rarer, like the elephant family, and big game in general.

Science-fiction writers often assume that there is a danger of man being replaced as the most dominant type by some other kind of creature—rats or ants are often suggested. There is really no possibility of this. So long as the human species continues to exist, the same qualities which secured its rise to biological dominance will continue to safeguard its position. War might destroy our civilization, change of climate might necessitate radical changes in human life, but it is not, I think, possible for any other species to threaten man's evolutionary dominance.

There is no case on record of a succession of deployments being reversed—no case where an older deployment has reacquired the capacity for progress, or succeeded in replacing its successor as dominant type. Furthermore, the facts of paleontology demonstrate that progressive lines, all those that were destined to give rise to new large-scale successful deployments, generally start low down on the branching system of the groups that they are eventually going to replace— that is to say, before specialization and restriction have gone very far. Thus the proto-reptiles arose very early in the history of amphibians, and the proto-mammals were already in existence less than half-way through the reptilian deployment, long before the latest brands of dinosaurs and other dominant reptiles came into being.

Put in another way, the ancestors of new deployments are always generalized, in the sense of being capable of transformation in many directions on a new level of existence, though they may have to wait a long time for the opportunity of realizing their possibilities. The lung-fish retained a primitive body-form which cut them off from success in the water, but permitted land locomotion later. The early mammals were generalized in their dentition and the structure of their limbs. Ancestral man had a generalized brain capable of adjusting behaviour to many environments and ways of life, while the true apes became more and more restricted.

Purely biological progress, in fact, has come to an end, but human progress is just beginning. There is a radical difference between them, which is correlated with the equally radical difference between any kind of animal life and any kind of human life. We begin by minimizing the difference between animals and ourselves by unconsciously projecting our own qualities into them: this is the way of children and of primitive peoples. Though early scientific thinkers, like Descartes, tried to make the difference absolute, later applications of the method of scientific analysis to man have, until quite recently, tended to reduce it again. This is partly because we have often been guilty of the fallacy of mistaking origins for explanations—what we may call the "nothing but" fallacy: if sexual impulse is at the base of love, then love is to be regarded as nothing but sex; if it can be shown that man originated from an animal, then in all essentials he is nothing but an animal. This, I repeat, is a dangerous fallacy.

We have tended to misunderstand the nature of the difference between ourselves and animals. We have a way of thinking that if there is continuity in time there must be continuity in quality. A little reflection would show that this is not the case. When we boil water there is a continuity of substance between water as a liquid and water as steam; but there is a critical point at which the substance H_2O changes its properties. This emergence of new properties is even more obvious when the process involves change in organization, as in all cases when chemical elements combine to produce a chemical compound.

The critical point in the evolution of man—the change of state when wholly new properties emerged in evolving life—was when he acquired the use of verbal concepts and could organize his experience in a common pool. It was this which made human life different from that of all other organisms; and we can now begin to grasp the nature and profundity of the difference. The development of animals is always closed; their evolution is always sooner or later restricted. Man's individual development, on the other hand, is potentially open. It continues throughout his life, and it can take place in all sorts of directions; while in animals there is only one normal pattern to be realized. The same sort of thing holds for man as a type —his pooled experience can be indefinitely added to, and it can be organized in an indefinite number of different ways. Animal types have limited possibilities, and sooner or later exhaust them: man has an unlimited field of possibilities, and he can never realize all of them. He has developed a new method of evolution: the transmission of organized experience by way of tradition, which supplements and largely overrides the automatic process of natural selection as the agency of change in the human phase.

This puts mind, in all its aspects, into the business of evolution. Thus, under this new dispensation, beliefs are inevitably brought into being; and once they have been brought into being, they become tools of living. And the same is true of ideals or purposes or scientific theories or religious systems—they are among the emergent properties of the new, human type of organization. They cannot help coming into existence, and then they cannot help becoming operative factors for further change. Thus, once life had become organized in human form it was impelled forward, not merely by the blind forces of natural selection but by mental and spiritual forces as well.

In the light of evolutionary biology man can now see himself as the sole agent of further evolutionary advance on this planet, and one of the few possible instruments of progress in the universe at large. He finds himself in the unexpected position of business manager for the cosmic process of evolution. He no longer ought to feel separated from the rest of nature, for he is part of it— that part which has become conscious, capable of love and understanding and aspiration. He need no longer regard himself as insignificant in relation to the cosmos. He is intensely significant. In his person, he has acquired meaning, for he is constantly creating new meanings. Human society generates new mental and spiritual agencies, and sets them to work in the cosmic process: it controls matter by means of mind.

It is not true that the nature of things is irrelevant to the interests of man, for the interests of man turn out to be part of the nature of things. Nor is it true that science cannot be concerned with values. Science is a method of enquiry which can be applied in all kinds of fields. In any particular field it has to deal with the subject-matter it finds there. In biology it can do something towards explaining the origins of conscious evaluation. But as soon as it is applied to man, it finds values among its data; you cannot either understand or control human affairs without taking them into account. For a science of man, the problem is not whether or no to have anything to do with values, but how to devise satisfactory methods of studying them and discovering how they work. Here again the operative method, the study of how processes happen, is the most likely one to yield positive results.

And so, in human life, the fact of progress is linked with the problem of destiny, in its dual sense of something to be obeyed and something to be fulfilled. Man alone is conscious of destiny; human organization is so constructed as to make men pose the problem of existence in this form. Ever since he first began, man has been groping to discern the features of his destiny more clearly. In the light of the evidence now available, he could come to the realization that his destiny is to participate and lead in the creative process of evolution, whereby new possibilities can be realized for life.

To draw this general conclusion appears to me as a real advance in thought. But it still remains to explore its implications and to study the means by which we might achieve in practice something of this destiny which is being revealed to us.

CHAPTER VI

The Human Phase

I CAN think of no other saying more pregnantly apt to the subject of this last chapter of mine than this of Walt Whitman's in his "Song of the Open Road": "All parts away for the progress of souls ... Of the progress of the souls of men and women along the grand roads of the Universe, all other progress is the needed emblem and sustenance." It is couched in evolutionary terms; it is based on the postulate of progress; it brings out the value of symbols in supporting human effort; and above all it sets forth the soul, which in this context is to be equated with the individual personality at its highest and fullest, as the ultimate standard by which we must judge all other human achievements.

Medieval theology urged men to think of human life in the light of eternity—*sub specie aeternitatis*: I am attempting to rethink it *sub specie evolutionis*—in the light of evolution. I do this, I confess, in some trepidation: but the trepidation is balanced by confidence: I rely on the truth of the facts and ideas discovered by thousands on thousands of patient workers. What I can do is to suggest some necessary items for the agenda of the great discussion, in which we can all co-operate.

Psycho-social evolution—human history for short—operates by cultural transmission; and its units are communities based on different types of culture. I am neither an anthropologist nor a sociologist; so, luckily, my readers will not expect me to define terms like *culture* and *community* with any precision. I am a biologist, and as such I see human history as a recent and very special outgrowth of biological evolution. Without the biological background, it looks different. In particular, it looks different in the perspective of evolutionary time. To the historical specialist, the five or six thousand years of civilization seem intolerably long. But this is a minute interval to the biologist. Man is very young: the human deployment is in an explosive and very early phase. Man is the result of two thousand million years of biological evolution: he has every prospect of an equal or even greater span of psycho-social evolution before him. The human species has many grave problems before it: but it has a great deal of time in which to work them out—there may be some comfort in that thought.

The biologist knows how fruitful has been the study of the mechanisms of genetic transmission for understanding the process of biological evolution. He can properly suggest to the humanist that a study of the mechanisms of cultural transmission will be equally fruitful for understanding the process of human history. Ideas, rituals, symbols, transmissible skills, beliefs, works of art—these seem to be the chief vehicles of this transmission. In addition to the self-reproduction and self-variation of material substance, in the shape of genes, we now have to consider the self-reproduction and self-variation of mental activities, operating through the various media of cultural inheritance. Our analysis of biological evolution as a process has brought out a number of important facts and ideas—improvement, finite steps of advance, deployment, and the rest. The biologist knows that they will not be directly applicable in detail to cultural evolution, but he can be sure that they have their human analogies, and that equally important ideas will emerge from the study of human history as an overall unitary process, ideas which will escape detection so long as history is treated merely as a record of separate sequences of events. The Marxists have tried to avoid any such parochialism, and to treat history as a general subject. Unfortunately they approach it from a too-limited outlook, and without taking into account the relevant analogies from evolutionary biology. Unesco is now embarking on the same task in a broader spirit: let us hope that their History of Mankind will be the first truly scientific and comprehensive account of psycho-social evolution as a process.

Now for some facts. Thanks to its new mechanism of operation, human deployment, since the time of the prehistoric cave-artists and before, differs in a very curious way from all other deployments throughout evolution. The single stock which has expanded in such a spectacular fashion has not broken up into separate species: the entire deployment takes place within the limits of one interbreeding group, without biological discontinuity. This was not always so. Let me remind you that, in the evolution of mammals, we could distinguish a group of pre-mammals as their reptilian forerunners; a group of proto-mammals as the not very successful, and of necessity transitional, first essays in mammalhood; and the full or true mammals, from which the new dominant deployment finally sprang. We can distinguish the same three stages in the physical evolution of man. First, the deployment of the pre-men. The original stock of pre-human apes differentiated into many species, all showing a trend towards what has been called hominization—the acquisition of more human characters. The recently discovered remains of Australopithecine apes from South Africa may perhaps represent some of the later side-branches of this deployment.

Next came the proto-men—with their bigger brains, their wonderful discovery of fire, their new capacity to make tools and implements and clothing, and doubtless some kind of true speech and social ritual; but still a long way from any large-scale deployment. The broad picture of their history which emerges from modern discoveries is something like this. They flourished especially in the earlier part of the Pleistocene, though some of them lingered on till near the end of the period, and the group certainly originated well before its beginning. All of them are now extinct. They include the famous Pekin man, and Pithecanthropus the Java ape-man, and the giant man from China, which are different enough from ourselves to be classed in different genera, and types such as Heidelberg and Neanderthal man, which are only distinct enough to be classified as different species. All of them seem to have been biologically discontinuous, like the separate species of the modern horse-family, though perhaps the discontinuity was not always quite complete: for instance, it is possible that Neanderthal man could still exchange genes with our own species. In any case, they constituted a typical divergent radiation.

And then we reach the fully human phase—man in the proper sense of the word. This was initiated, perhaps a quarter of a million years ago, with the evolution of our own species—*Homo sapiens* according to the rules of zoological nomenclature. This single group of individuals eventually gave rise to the whole of humanity, with its tribes and nations, its civilizations and empires. But it had to await its evolutionary opportunity. It dragged on as a numerically small group for perhaps four-fifths of the time since its origin; and then, towards the very end of the last Ice Age, the human deployment really began, as a major process of expansion which turned man from an unimportant minor branch into a new dominant group. The expansion of the new type began in the orthodox way, by slow spatial spread over the continents, followed by physical divergence into sub-species, adapted to different climates and regions. These sub-species were markedly distinct—the proto-types of the main races of man, black, yellow, and white; but they never diverged to complete discontinuity—they never went on to become fully separate species. Thanks to man's migratory urge and his psychological adaptability, divergence began to give place to convergence: the genes that had been separated out were brought together again by intercrossing, and the tendency towards discontinuity was reversed. The process of convergence was accentuated after the close of the Ice Age, by the recurrent migrations and irruptions of prehistoric and historic times. Though there are still barriers against so-called race crossing, the whole human deployment has become increasingly a single interbreeding unit, instead of an increasing number of non-interbreeding units.

The same process of divergence followed by convergence occurred on the cultural level. The tendency to sharp differentiation of cultures is a striking feature of human history. The ancient Mediterranean was a patchwork of contrasting cultures; Aztec culture was as different from European as a horse is from a dog; and studies like those of Ruth Benedict and Margaret Mead demonstrate the radical difference between different kinds and levels of cultural organization existing today. But the contrary tendency is equally striking: separation is offset by inter-communication and cultural interchange. The general tendency of the past few centuries has been to intensify this trend. We can already see the inevitable outline of the future—the emergence of a single world community. Even the barriers to exchange that have recently been set up are in a sense symptoms of the trend, reactions against its force.

Cultural interchange does not necessarily result in cultural uniformity. The world community which we envisage and hope to bring to the birth is a variety-in-unity. In the useful phrase of the American writer, L. K. Frank, it involves an orchestration of cultures.

The process of human deployment is unique in this tendency to overcome divergence by convergent integration. It is also unique in another respect—the form of its curves of change. If you were to plot biological changes against evolutionary time on a graph, they would tend to fall along a series of straight lines (though with explosive beginnings and stable ends). But many of the changes of cultural evolution accelerate themselves; they curve upwards at a constantly increasing rate until they come up against some barrier. French scientists have coined the term *surexpansion*—superexpansion—to denote this process. This applies to the growth of human population as well as to cultural phenomena in the ordinary sense. Most educated people now know that the total number of human beings has increased more or less steadily from early prehistoric times to the present, and that each year more people are being added to the population than were added the year before (the present figure is about twenty-two millions). But very few, I believe, realize that the rate of increase has itself been steadily increasing. If you think of world population in terms of a sum of money increasing at compound interest, the interest rate itself has increased around twenty-fold—from, perhaps, one-half of one-tenth per cent. in the hunting phase at the close of the Ice Age, to close on one per cent. today. And there is no sign of its decrease in the near future. The result is that population is pressing increasingly hard on resources; and the further result is that, during the past few centuries, at least, world population as a whole has come to contain vast numbers of under-nourished and therefore sub-normally developed individuals. Human fertility is now the greatest long-term threat to human standards, spiritual as well as material.

And there are standards in human evolution. One school of anthropologists is never tired of proclaiming the doctrines of cultural relativity—that different cultures are not higher nor lower, but merely adjusted in different ways. But this is to neglect the lessons of biology. To take an extreme example, no biologist doubts that the spiny ant-eater is a survivor of the primitive proto-mammalian type, although we can be sure that none of the original proto-mammals had long prickly spines and a specialized ant-eating mouth and tongue. In the same way, I should say there can be no doubt that the social and cultural organization of the Australian black-fellows is a survival of a very low and primitive type of culture, even though some features of it, like the intricate details of its totems and its marriage system, are clearly a recent specialization.

As with animal types, in fact, so with cultures; advance is a more important criterion than mere survival. A progressive culture is one which contains the seeds of its own further transformation, and cultures which are not in some way related to the general trends of the human process may be a drag on the advance of humanity as a whole, and may have to be preserved as living fossils if they are to be saved from extinction. So too with morality, our beliefs about right and wrong. Certainly morality is always relative, but its ultimate relationship is to our beliefs about human destiny as a whole. As with biological evolution, we need to look at the mechanism and process of cultural evolution in the broadest possible way, for only so will its general features emerge clearly from the welter of facts.

One generalization is that psycho-social evolution, like biological evolution, goes in a series of well-marked steps. Another is that in all stages of cultural organization, mental and material factors are interrelated, and both sets of factors are operative. It is clear that the change-over from an agricultural to an industrial system was a decisive step in human affairs; but so was the passage from a belief in magic and witchcraft to the scientific approach. In actual practice, there is often a time-lag between the two kinds of factors. Beliefs may persist as effective social agencies long after the economic conditions to which they were originally related have passed away, as with the Divine Rights of Kings. And material and social conditions may prove resistant to the best of ideas over centuries of time: the Christian idea of the essential equality of all men could not exert its full effect before new systems of production permitted the abolition of slavery and serfdom.

The dominant beliefs of a community may have decisive effects on the lives of its members or on its own development. Thus the erroneous belief that death is never natural but is always attributable to some kind of witchcraft has led to the witch-smelling ordeals of Africa and has resulted in suffering or death for countless thousands of her people. The ancient Egyptians believed that kings and important personages could be made to live on in an after-life, but that their continued survival there could only be ensured by continuing to provide them with real or symbolic nourishment. This belief eventually changed the economic life of the country, by transferring an increasing proportion of the land from more efficient exploitation under the kings to less efficient exploitation by colleges of priests.

It is easy enough to make broad statements about the steps of advance which have transformed the quality of human life and experience. We have the technical steps —the step from food-gathering to hunting; the domestication of animals and plants; the invention of the wheel and of building in stone; the development of urban life; the invention first of writing, then of alphabetic writing; and so on to the familiar triumphs of modern applied science. We also have the steps in the organization of thought and creative expression; the passage from thinking exclusively in terms of magic to thinking also in terms of gods; the origin of philosophy from mythology and of drama from ritual; the pursuit of learning for its own sake; the rise of the scientific method of enquiry. That, I repeat, is all too easy. What is difficult is to discover just how any one step is effected, still more to distinguish desirable from undesirable change, and restrictive from non-restrictive improvement.

That is the job of the science of man. Perhaps, I should say, the job of the human sciences, from psychology to history, from ethnology to economics, for there is as yet no single science of man, in the sense of an organized branch of enquiry with a common body of postulates and ideas. It is, I think, fair to say that the human sciences today are somewhat in the position occupied by the biological sciences in the early 1800's; they are rapidly exploring different sectors of their field, but still looking for a central core of general principles. One idea which came into my mind during the writing of this chapter was that, in the human phase of evolution, the struggle for existence has been largely superseded, as an operative force, by the struggle for fulfilment. It is the combination of these two terms which seems to me important. Human life *is* a struggle —against frustration, ignorance, suffering, evil, the maddening inertia of things in general; but it is also a struggle *for* something, and for something which our experience tells us can be achieved in some measure, even if we personally find ourselves debarred from any measure that seems just or reasonable. And fulfilment seems to describe better than any other single word the positive side of human development and human evolution—the realization of inherent capacities by the individual and of new possibilities by the race; the satisfaction of needs, spiritual as well as material; the emergence of new qualities of experience to be enjoyed; the building of personalities. But it cannot be achieved without struggle, not merely struggle with external obstacles, but with the enemies within our own selves.

There is also a struggle with the new problems that the process of change is always throwing up. To quote

Whitman once more: "It is provided in the essence of things that from any fruition of success shall come forth something to make a greater struggle necessary." But the obverse of struggle is satisfaction; and satisfaction in the free enjoyment of one's own capacities is another essential thread in human life. Of course, not all fulfilment or all enjoyment is good or right, any more than all biological improvement is progressive. It is the business of moral systems to make such evaluations. But something of their goodness or rightness emerges when they are considered in conjunction with another key idea, that of participation.

The idea of participation in a common task, as against competition for slices in a limited cake, has already become widely current. We are getting accustomed to the idea of the participation of different nations in common jobs like defence, or the exploitation of natural resources, or the raising of the general standard of life. The idea can readily be given greater force and greater range by extending it to mean participation in the overall adventure of evolution. It then applies as much to realization of possibilities by the single individual as to human destiny as a whole. Other key ideas which emerged from our study of biological evolution were *flexibility* and *integration*. They are, I maintain, of general application in every aspect of human life, from personality to social structure.

Keeping these key ideas at the back of my mind, I shall devote the rest of my space to a few aspects of the human phase of evolution. The aspects I should choose as most important are as follows: the importance of knowledge and the organization of knowledge in the process of psycho-social transformation; the principle of limited but increasing certitude, as illustrated by scientific method; the ultimate wrongness of absolutism, in ideas as well as politics; the primacy of the human individual; and the need to keep human development open for the realization of new possibilities. These are all interconnected, each in a two-way relation with all the others, and it is impossible to present them briefly as part of a single sequence of argument. So I am reduced merely to outlining my themes as part of a total pattern of approach, trusting to my listeners to fill in the logical gaps.

A first principle, it seems to me, is one which has come up again and again in previous chapters—the fact that progressive evolution involves the realization of new possibilities, but that this only occurs to the accompaniment of imperfections of every kind. This realization of new possibilities has continued during human evolution, though to the accompaniment of appalling suffering and frustration. As with biological evolution, the immediate view reveals mainly the struggle and the imperfections, and the short-term view mainly the dead ends and the failures: but once you look at the process as a whole, a general direction becomes apparent. So we must believe in our own possibilities, both individually and collectively, while at the same time accepting our limitations. Our practical job is to keep human development open, to see how much fulfilment is possible, and how to reduce the amount of frustration.

A second major concept is the primacy of the human individual, or, to use a better term, the primacy of personality. This primacy of human personality has been, in different ways, a *postulate* both of Christianity and of liberal democracy: but it is a *fact* of evolution. By whatever objective standard we choose to take, properly developed human personalities are the highest products of evolution; they have greater capacities and have reached a higher level of organization than any other parts of the world substance.

Both of these ideas, in one form or another, have played important roles in history. The combination of the two in a broad evolutionary approach leads to a further thesis, that the nearest to an ultimate that we can discern in human life is not an absolute, but a trend —the trend towards greater realization of possibilities by means of the co-operation of integrated individual personalities. That sounds rather a mouthful; but once our minds have digested it, a great deal else falls into place. First of all, it clarifies the relations between the individual and society. Society is seen as existing for the individual, not vice versa. Social and cultural organizations, including the State, are necessary as instruments of order and vehicles of transmission and continuity in human life, but their most significant function is to provide means whereby more of its members enjoy richer fulfilment. If a society permits large numbers of its citizens to grow up without the means of enjoying beauty, or of developing their minds, it is not performing its functions adequately.

Next point: the individual has duties not only to society but to himself—or perhaps I should say to the possibilities that are in him. It is true that one aspect of his fulfilment lies in working for others; but another aspect consists in his enjoyments and the free exercise of his capacities. For after all, it is only through human individuals that the evolutionary process reaches its highest and most varied achievements. Each time you enjoy a sunset or a symphony, each time you understand an interesting fact or idea, each time you find satisfaction in making something, or in disciplined activity like sport, evolution has brought another of its possibilities to fruition.

Of course, the possibilities of man's inner life are as important as those of his active existence. The achievement of inner harmony in the building up of the personality is as important as was the development of self-regulating mechanisms in the evolution of the animal body.

K

This leads on to the subject of morality. Morality in the usual sense of the word is concerned with something outside the self—the individual's relations with others, with God, with society as a whole. But this needs relating with a morality concerned with the self—the rightness of free creative activity, of personal fulfilment. Psychiatrists like the American Erich Fromm have developed this idea in a very interesting way. And finally, for the evolutionary biologist, both must be related with a third sort of morality—the rightness or wrongness of the relation between man and his future. From this angle, anything which permits or promotes open development is right, anything which restricts or frustrates development is wrong. It is a morality of evolutionary direction. Here again, the Americans seem to be doing more than anyone else to explore the subject—I think of philosophers such as Charles Morris, with his book *The Open Self* (Prentice-Hall, New York).

Now I must pass to another of my main themes. Since man's evolution operates via his pooled experience, it is clear that the acquisition and the organization of knowledge are essential factors in the process. During the past three centuries a new general method of acquiring and organizing knowledge has been invented, or perhaps we had better say perfected—what is usually called the scientific method; and this, wherever it has been fully applied, has proved its superiority over all other methods. It operates on what we may call the principle of limited but increasing certitude, always ready to test its conclusions against experience by way of observation or experiment, but able in large measure to take effective action and to proceed to new subjects of enquiry on the basis of the facts and ideas already established. It thus combines flexibility with assurance in a unique way.

In scientific enquiry, different detailed methods are required for different subject-fields—those of physics and chemistry are inadequate to explore the fields of psychology and animal behaviour. For a long time there was resistance to applying scientific method to the study of man. Now that a beginning has been made in the field of human affairs, we are finding out how much more complex this is than any other, and are having to work out all kinds of new methods for dealing with it; but there is no reason to doubt the eventual efficacy of the scientific principle of limited but increasing certitude in this field any more than in any other. In any case, we have to make the attempt. It is an essential method for keeping the process of understanding the world an open one, without restrictions on its growth.

This leads to my next point—the intrinsic wrongness of absolutism. It is generally accepted in the western world that political absolutism—totalitarian government—is inherently bad, because it degrades the individual from the dignity of a free agent to the position of a slave, and substitutes commands and force for willing co-operation. It is bad because it considers individuals only as the means to an end, never as ends in themselves. But it is also bad because of its effects on knowledge. One way in which absolute power corrupts is this—the more absolute it is, the more it tends to invade freedom of thought and enquiry, and, indeed, the freedom of art and literature as well; we have only to remind ourselves of what happened in Nazi Germany, and what has been happening in the U.S.S.R. during the past twenty years. And freedom of thought and enquiry and creative expression are necessary prerequisites for anything that we can consider as a full human life or as a social advance.

To me, as an evolutionary biologist, the handling of the Lysenko controversy in the U.S.S.R. has been inherently wrong. This is not merely because the Lysenkoist views are scientifically untenable, and yet are being shielded from the free scientific criticism they would receive elsewhere; not merely because the up-shot has been that the promising unity of world science has been disrupted; but because a political party has imposed its own dogmatic view of what must be correct and incorrect, and so violated the essential spirit of science.

In the same sort of way, I cannot help regarding official Catholic pronouncements on birth control and sex relations as inherently wrong. They are wrong because population increase is, together with war, the greatest present threat to civilization and progress; because, in so far as they are implemented in practice, they mean frustration and misery and ill-health and ignorance, not for millions but for thousands of millions of human souls; and because they would result in general failure to realize higher possibilities for mankind as a whole. But to me they are also wrong because they are asserted absolutely and dogmatically, instead of being conclusions arrived at by free enquiry as to what is best to do in particular circumstances. That the subject can be fruitfully approached in this way is shown by the recent Royal Commission on Population and the studies made by the Church of England.

One obvious task for the free world to undertake is the scientific exploration of human possibilities. This has of course begun—to take but two examples, in the study of educational methods and of psychological capacities. But it has not yet been undertaken scientifically and systematically, from the point of view of exploring possibilities in general rather than establishing a number of isolated facts and conclusions. Immense opportunities are open. Thus, wrong methods of teaching may result in boredom and frustration and general distrust of one's own capacities. But right methods, as the studies of Piaget have shown even for the teaching of mathematics, show how education can be increasingly turned into a process of self-fulfilment. The mass of data gathered from children's art shows what important possibilities of self-realization are here available, and also shows how they are being neglected in all but a tiny fraction of developing human beings. The greatest opportunities, however, would seem to lie in applying scientific method to the exploration of man's inner life. The experiences of the mystics of all creeds and of the practitioners of Yoga prove what transcendent states of inner peace and unity of spirit the human personality is capable of. The systematic study of these possibilities of spiritual development would hold out the hope of devising techniques for making them more generally attainable.

But we must have a realistic background for all such explorations. We must face the fact that now, in this year of grace 1951, the great majority of human beings are sub-standard: they are under-nourished, or ill, or condemned to a ceaseless struggle for bare existence; they are imprisoned in ignorance or superstition. Here the possibilities are obvious enough, but they have not been realized in practice. This is the great reproach on the world's conscience. But once the terrible fact is properly grasped, it can become an incentive. We must see to it that life is no longer a hell paved with unrealized opportunity. The further fact that vast fields of possibility still remain unexplored adds inspiration and hope to incentive and duty. In this light the highest and most sacred duty of man is seen as the proper utilization of the untapped resources of human beings.

I find myself inevitably driven to use the language of religion. For the fact is that all this does add up to something in the nature of a religion: perhaps one might call it Evolutionary Humanism. The word "religion" is often used restrictively to mean belief in gods; but I am not using it in this sense—I certainly do not want to see man erected into the position of a god, as happened with many individual human beings in the past and is happening still today. I am using it in a broader sense, to denote an overall relation between man and his destiny, and one involving his deepest feelings, including his sense of what is sacred. In this broad sense, evolutionary humanism, it seems to me, is capable of becoming the germ of a new religion, not necessarily supplanting existing religions but supplementing them. It remains to see how this germ could be developed—to work out its intellectual framework, to see how its ideas could be made inspiring, to ensure their wide diffusion. Above all, it would be necessary to justify ideas by facts—to find the areas of frustration and point out where they were being reduced; to show how research into human possibilities was providing new incentives for their realization, as well as demonstrating the means for realizing them.

You may have been surprised that I have not mentioned eugenic possibilities; and indeed I must say a word about them. In the human phase, the biological mechanisms of evolution—physical heredity and natural selection—are now subsidiary to the psycho-social ones. Though undoubtedly man's genetic nature changed a great deal during the long proto-human stage, there is no evidence that it has been in any important way improved since the time of the Aurignacian cave-men. What has been improved since then are the tools of action and thought and the ways of accumulating and utilizing experience: and these improvements have had truly prodigious results in a very brief period of time. Indeed, during this period it is probable that man's genetic nature has degenerated and is still doing so. In general, the more elaborate social life is, the more it tends to shield individuals from the action of natural selection; and when this occurs, as we have already seen, harmful mutations accumulate instead of being weeded out. As a result of this process, there can be no reasonable doubt that the human species today is burdened with many more deleterious mutant genes than can possibly exist in any species of wild creature.

There is also the fact that modern industrial civilization favours the differential decrease of the genes concerned with intelligence. It seems now to be established that, both in communist Russia and in most capitalist countries, people with higher intelligence have, on the average, a lower reproductive rate than the less intelligent; and that some of this difference is genetically determined. The genetic differences are slight, but as I pointed out in my second chapter, such slight differences speedily multiply to produce large effects. If this process were to continue, the results would be extremely grave. Society needs more intelligent people for the more difficult jobs, and we certainly ought to see what could be done to reverse the trend.

But eugenics is not merely a matter of stopping deterioration; it can also be aimed at securing further improvement. After all, we know that artificial selection can be much more effective and can get results much more quickly than natural selection. By artificial selection, man has pushed both the speed and the strength of horses well beyond the point that nature was able to reach, and he was able to do so in a paltry ten thousand years or less. On theoretical grounds, we could certainly breed up a number of specialized human types if we set our minds to it. But if the general argument of this chapter is sound, we cannot think along these lines. The essence of man's success as an organism is that he has not evolved as a set of separate specialized types, but has kept all his genes in a common interbreeding pool, and he cannot afford to break up this genetic continuity. However, that does not preclude the possibility of a general improvement. Eugenics for general improvement does not mean trusting the State or any other authority with some arbitrary power for deciding what are good and what are bad hereditary qualities. There is really no difficulty in agreeing that certain hereditary characteristics are generally desirable—greater physical vigour, less liability to specific defects and diseases, greater general intelligence, various special aptitudes. If we could raise the average of these characteristics by even 5 or 10 per cent., an almost incalculable burden of suffering and frustration would be lifted from human shoulders, and an enormous field of opportunity would be opened up.

What is more, the geneticist knows that with appropriate methods such a result could be achieved over a measurable series of generations. Admittedly, this could not happen without somewhat radical changes in customs and laws and outlook; but this does not mean that it is impossible. Once the fact is grasped that we men are the agents of further evolution, and that there can be no action higher or more noble than raising the inherent possibilities of life, ways and means will somehow be found for overcoming any resistances that stand in the way of that realization. At the moment, large-scale eugenics is outside the range of practical possibility; but already, on the basis of our present knowledge, the eugenic idea can become an incentive and a hope.

What I have aimed at in this little book has been to give some sort of map of the evolutionary process as a whole. This was probably an impossible task, and I have certainly found it a very difficult one to execute to my own satisfaction. I have had to leave out such an enormous amount of evidence, and to skip so much of the analysis and the argument. That does not matter if I have given you some feeling of the unity and sweep of the process, some sense of its broad trends, some understanding of the general forces at work in it: above all, if I have helped to give you some insight into its nature as a self-transforming process, constantly generating new patterns and novel qualities, building its future by transcending its past.

In the long run, our actions are related to our overall picture, our map of reality. Any picture which leaves out the facts of evolution will be an incomplete and untrue picture, and will, sooner or later, lead us astray in our actions. Even an insect like a bee has to build up a three-dimensional map of the country round its hive to find its way about. It is in relation to the total picture of its surroundings that it steers itself in space. But man's surroundings are enormously larger, and in them he has to steer himself in time as well as in space. That is why his map must be a four-dimensional one. A three-dimensional map will help him to determine his position and chart his direction, but a four-dimensional one will also help him in choosing his destination.

But enough of cartographical metaphors. Human history and human destiny are part of a larger process. Only by getting some overall view of reality, in its dual aspect of self-transforming pattern and continuing process, can man hope to get a clearer view of his place —his unique place—in the process, and steer a better course into the future. This is my firm conviction, and if I have succeeded in any degree in persuading my readers of its validity, I shall be content.

INDEX

acquired characters, 40
adaptation, 18, 50
advance, evolutionary, 65, 81
algae, 19
allels, 26
amber, 128
Ammonites, 61, 70n.
Anableps, 50
Anopheles, 72
Antedon, 21
antelopes, 64
ants, perception in, 98; persistence of type, 128
apes, 31, 101; learning in, 104
Archaeopteryx, 64
Argus pheasant, 51
art, 108
arthropods, 19, 120
ascidians, 22, 74
Australopithecine apes, 136
awareness, 93
axolotl, 30

bacteria, 19, 23, 25, 26, 43, 44n., 73, 88
Baldwin, 41
bats, ultra-sonic sense, 93
Beer, G. R. de, *Embryos and Ancestors*, 30
bees, vision, 93; language, 103
beetles, learning capacity, 100
behaviourism, 89

Benedict, Ruth, 138
birds, 124
birth control, 148
blindness, effects of, 97
bones, 41
Bury, Professor, *The Idea of Progress*, 112

camouflage, 90
Cantril, Professor H., 98
carbon chains, 25
Carnivora, 72
cave fish, 43
cells, 117
Cenozoic, 32
Ceratodus (Neoceratodus, 112), 127
cerebral cortex, 15, 59, 80, 91
characters, consequential, 53; correlated, 53
chiffchaff, 70
chimpanzees, 97; behaviour, 106
chromosomes, 15, 16, 26, 117
colour, 34; perception of, 58
colour-blindness, 90
colour-vision, 90
concepts, 34
conflict, mental, 107
conscience, 107
convergence, in human evolution, 138
courtship, mutual, 96
crows, 71
cultural transmission, 17, 134 f.

dandelions, 43n.

Darwin, Charles, 35, 38, 39, 40, 53, 54, 66; *The Origin of Species*, 67; *The Expression of the Emotions in Man and Animals*, 104, 112

death, 130

degeneration, 43, 74

Demerec, 43

deployment, 66, 76, 128

Descartes, 131

destiny, 133

dingo, 69

dinosaurs, 78

displacement behaviour, 96

divergence, in human evolution, 138

Divine Right (of Kings), 141

dominant groups, 33

dragonfly, 64, 75

Drosophila, 27, 28, 29, 41, 46, 70

earthworms, 74, 92, 101

Echidna, 78

echinoderms, 19, 119

Eddington, Sir Arthur, 13

Egypt, ancient, 141

electric eel, 89

Eohippus, 55

eugenics, 150

Euglena, 92

evolution, general, 12; inorganic, 13; biological, 14; human, 16, 134n.; time-scale of, 31; irreversibility of, 37; rate of, 60

evolutionary opportunity, 53, 56, 67, 115

eye, 75

ferns, 19

filter-feeders, 73

Fisher, Professor R. A., 46

flat-fish, 21

flatworms, 118

flexibility, 143

flickers, 71

fossils, 31

fowls, 29; frizzled, 45; learning in, 100

Frank, L. K., 138

Frisch, von, 103

Fritillaria, 16

Fromm, E., 146

fungi, 19, 73

Galapagos Islands, 67, 72, 128n.

game-birds, behaviour, 95

Gammarus, 29

Garstang, W., 119

geese, behaviour, 102

gene-complex, 28

generation, spontaneous, 23

genes, 15, 26, 117; and development, 28; mutant, 38

genetics, 26

Geospizidae, 67

germ-plasm, 120

gill-clefts, 20, 21, 22

Gingko, 22, 127

gradients, in development, 30

grebe, courtship behaviour, 96

groundfinches, 67, 72, 128n.

ground-sloth, 129

gulls, behaviour, 95, 101

Hadzi, Professor, 118

Haeckel, E., 21

haemophilia, 42
Haldane, Professor J. B. S., 125
Hawaii, 68
head, evolution of, 119
Hebb, Professor, *The Organization of Behaviour*, 100
Hinshelwood, Sir C., 44n.
Homo sapiens, 137
Hormones, 30
Horses, 37n., 63; evolution of, 55n.
Hoyle, Fred, *The Nature of the Universe*, 13
Humanism, evolutionary, 149
Huxley, T. H., 126

Ice Age, 32
ichneumon-fly, 82
ichthyosaurs, 37n.
illusions, 97
"imprinting," 102
improbability, apparent, 46
improvement, 39, 62, 81, 113
independence, biological, 114
individuality, 144
Infusoria, 23
insects, 30; respiration of, 76; behaviour, 102, 120
instincts, 102
integration, 114, 143

jackdaw, 99, 105, 106, 111
Jeans, Sir James, 13
jellyfish, 19, 73

Keller, Helen, 109, 110
Koehler, Professor Otto, 106
Krogh, Professor, 76

Lack, David, *Darwin's Finches*, 68
Lamarckism, 40
land-life, evolution of, 122
Langer, Professor Suzanne, *Philosophy in a New Key*, 110
language, 34; human, 109; of bees, 109
Latimeria, 128
life, origin of, 23
light, perception of, 85
Lingula, 127
Linnaeus, 72
liver-fluke, 82
Lloyd-Morgan, C., 41, 100
Lorenz, Professor K., 101, 105
lung-fish, 33, 123, 127, 130
Lyell, 49
Lysenko, 40, 147

magic, 140
magpie, 100
mammals, 32, 123; deployment of, 79
man, evolution of, 125; method of evolution in, 132; subspecies, 137
marsupials, in Australia, 68
mathematics, 111
mayfly, 103
Mead, Margaret, 138
Meaning of Evolution, The (Simpson), 61, 114n.
melanism, in moths, 45
Mendel, 35
mental activity, 88
mental organization, 87, 91 f., 103
Mesozoic, 32, 33, 90, 123, 127

Metazoa, 118, 120
Michurinism, 40
Milton, *Paradise Lost*, 85
mind, evolution of, 87
mind and matter, 85 f.
molluscs, 19, 120
morality, 140, 146
Morris, Charles, 146
mosquitoes, 71
mosses, 19
moths, sense of smell, 94; melanism, 45
Muller, Professor H. J., 47
mutation, 27, 37n., 38, 41, 48
mutation-rate, 116
myriapods, 30, 119

natural selection, 15, 38, 51, 53
Neanderthal man, 137
nerve-net, 83
nervous system, 83
neurosis, in apes, 107
Newton, 35
nöosphere, 110
notochord, 20, 22

octopus, behaviour, 99
ontogeny, 20, 22
organic selection, 41
orthogenesis, 40, 55
oysters, 127

paedomorphosis, 119
pain, 88, 99
Paleozoic, 32
Paramecium, 91, 92
parasites, 82
parasitism, 74
parrots, 101
Pasteur, 23

pattern-vision, 34, 90
penicillin, 44
perception, organization of, 97; in ants, 98
persistence of type, 126
phylogeny, 21, 22
Piaget, 148
Pithecanthropus, 137
pit-vipers, 93
placentals, 68
planarians, 37
platypus, 77
play, 108
pollen-tube, 22
polyploidy, 28
population, 139, 148
pre-adaptation, 42
primates, colour-vision in, 90
progress, biological, 81, 112 f., 130; human, 130
proteins, 15
proto-mammals, 79, 130
protozoa, 18, 80, 117
pterodactyls, 124
puffins, 50
purpose, 15, 17

rabbits, 29, 69
radiation, adaptive, 32, 68
rats, learning capacity, 100
raven, 99
recapitulation, 16, 21
receptor organs, 93
recombination, 27
reflexes, conditioned, 100
releasers, 95; in man, 96
Rensch, Professor Bernhard, 75, 99
replacement, evolutionary, 77, 113, 129

repression, 107
reproduction, sexual, 23, 38, 49
reptiles, mesozoic, 33; dominance of, 78
robin, behaviour, 101
Ryle, Professor, 86

Sacculina, 82
scale insects, 44
science, and human possibilities, 148
sciences, human and biological, 142
scientific method, 143
sea-scorpions, 32
seed-plants, 19
selection, intensity of, 51
sensation, types of, 94
sex, genetics of, 29
Simpson, Dr. G. G.: *Horses*, 55; *The Meaning of Evolution*, 61, 114n., 127
size, consequential effect on learning, 99
snakes, 76
social organization, 145
soma, 120
specialization, 71, 74, 130
speciation, 70 f.
species, number of, 18; origin of, 70
sponges, 18, 73, 83, 118
stabilization, 65
State, the, 145
steam-engine, improvement of, 63
Stephenson: his *Rocket*, 63
stickleback, 96
streptomycin, 43

subspecies, 72
symmetry, bilateral, 119

Teilhard de Chardin, Père, 110
Teleosts, 128, 129
temperature-regulation, 34
tempo, of development, 30
tendons, 40
tentacle-feeders, 73
Thorpe, Dr. W. H., 41, 100, 101
Tinbergen, Dr. D. N., 95, 96
titanotheres, 53
tits, and milk-bottles, 102
tree-creepers, 70
Tridacna, 50
trilobites, 32
tropism, 92

Unesco, 136

values, 82, 133
variation, 39
vertebrates, 19, 32, 120; learning in, 102; progress in, 121
viruses, 18, 24
vision, binocular, 125; pattern, 34, 90; colour, 90

wagtails, 72
wasps, 100
water-boatmen, 44
water-flea, 42
weevils, 72
Weismann, A., 120
Westoll, Professor S. S., 66
whales, 37n., 73, 129

Whitman, Walt, 134, 143

willow-warbler, 70

worms, 19

Yoga, 149

Young, Professor J. Z., 99;
Doubt and Certainty in Science, 15

zebras, 60

Printed in Great Britain
by T. and A. CONSTABLE LTD., Hopetoun Street,
Printers to the University of Edinburgh